Job Practice Manual

Modern Masonry
Brick, Block, Stone

by

Clois E. Kicklighter

Dean, School of Technology
and Professor of Construction Technology
Indiana State University
Terra Haute, Indiana

Publisher
THE GOODHEART-WILLCOX COMPANY, INC.
Tinley Park, Illinois

Materials used for the cover courtesy of *Kimpling's Ace
Hardware*, Washington, Illinois; and *Builders Square*,
Homewood, Illinois.

Introduction

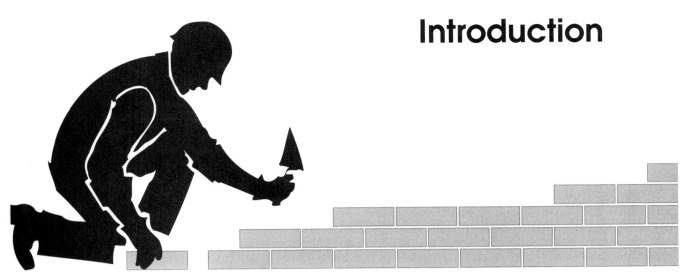

The **Job Practice Manual** is designed for use with **Modern Masonry—Brick, Block, Stone**. The jobs and review questions are designed to help you become a professional brick mason, block mason, stone mason, or cement finisher. Every job is related to the skills and knowledge that a professional mason must have to perform their duties. Most of the jobs are supported by additional information in the text in addition to the step-by-step procedures. A comprehensive list of the jobs covered in the manual is included in the contents section.

The jobs are action-oriented laboratory and field experiences that are designed to build skill and knowledge of accepted practices in the trade. They cover the areas specified in apprenticeship training programs. Each job is a stand-alone activity that can be undertaken in any preferred sequence, but they become more complex as the novice mason progresses through the jobs in the recommended sequence. Also, more detailed information is given in the beginning jobs than in later ones. Each job adds to the experience and lays the foundation for a more advanced experience in a related area.

The jobs are grouped into eight major categories: *General, Basic Operation, Brick Masonry, Block Masonry, Stone Masonry, Concrete Work, Form Construction*, and *Advanced Masonry Work*. The job categories are identified on the first page of each Job Practice with an icon in the upper-right corner. The icon is also used as a locating tabbing device. With this icon/tabbing device combination you are able to easily locate the beginning of a job and immediately determine the job category. The icons used in this Manual are as follows:

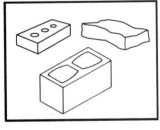

General

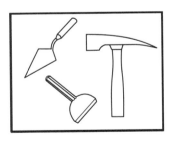

Basic Operation

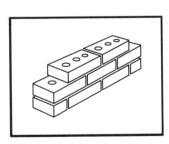

Brick Masonry

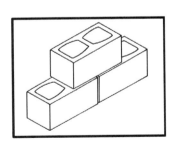

Block Masonry

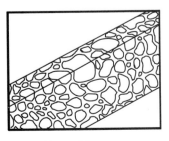

Stone Masonry

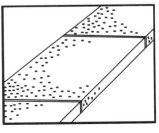

Concrete Work

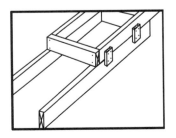

Form Construction

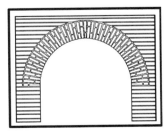

Advanced Masonry Work

The first two categories—*General* and *Basic Operation*—generally relate to most of the basic trade areas. They should be performed first whether one wishes to pursue brick masonry, block masonry, or stone masonry. After completing those jobs you can proceed to any of the other sections.

As with any profession, there is more than one way to perform most tasks. Each job presents one method of performing the task and does not imply that other procedures are not just as effective. The instructor can modify any procedure that they feel is advisable.

Each Job Practice identifies the title or description of the job, the category, the objective, the tools and equipment needed, and the recommended procedure for the job. Following the completion of the job, review questions are also included at the end of each job to serve as a reflective experience. Answers to the questions are included in the Instructor's Manual.

Although not a specific requirement, apprentice masons should be encouraged to purchase their own equipment. Using ones own equipment leads to better care and maintenance of it. This is also a necessary part of learning the trade. A list of the typical equipment for each trade area as well as equipment that should be provided by the school is included in this manual.

Mason's Tools

The following list of tools and equipment are presented as an aid to the apprentice mason. The basic tools listed in each trade area are representative of the tools most professionals use. The equipment is generally provided by the school for use in class activities.

Brick and block mason's tools

Blocking chisel
Brick set chisel
Buttering trowel
Chalk box
Convex jointer (long)
Convex jointer (short)
Cross joint trowel
Duckbill trowel
Flexible rule
Folding rule
Framing square

Gauging trowel
Line blocks
Line trigs (twigs)
Margin trowel
Mason's brush
Mason's hammer
Mason's line
Mason's tool bag
Mason's trowel
Modular spacing rule

Personal safety equipment
Plain joint raker
Plugging or joint chisel
Plumb bob
Plumb rule
Pointing trowel
Skate wheel joint raker
Slicker
V-jointer (long)
V-jointer (short)

Stone mason's tools:

Buttering trowel
Chalk box
Convex jointer (long)
Convex jointer (short)
Cross joint trowel
Duckbill trowel
Framing square
Folding rule
Flexible rule
Gauging trowel
Line blocks

Margin trowel
Mason's brush
Mason's hammer
Mason's line
Mason's tool bag
Mason's trowel
Metal trigs (twigs)
Personal safety equipment
Plain joint raker
Plumb bob
Plumb rule

Pointing trowel
Pry bar
Skate wheel joint raker
Sledge hammer
Slicker
Sponge
Steel wedges
Stone mason's chisels
Stone mason's hammer
V-jointer (long)
V-jointer (short)

Cement finisher's tools:

Bull float
Carpenter's hammer
Cement mason's hand trowel
Chalk box
Curb and gutter tools
Darby
Edgers (several sizes)
Flexible rule

Folding rule
Framing square
Hand float
Hand tamper
Jointers/groovers
Knee pads
Mason's hammer
Mason's line

Mason's trowel
Personal safety equipment
Plumb bob
Plumb rule
Screed
Step and corner tools
Tool bag
Wire cutters

Shop tools and equipment:

Air compressor
Angle sander/grinder
Brick tongs
Buckets
Cement mixer
Concrete placer/spreader
Concrete rake
Concrete vibrator
Contractor's level and rod
Contractor's wheelbarrow
Corner poles
Dirt tamper
Fork lift tractor
Grout bags
Hydraulic masonry splitter

Imprint roller
Jig saw
Ladders
Laser level
Masonry saw
Mixing box
Modular concrete forms
Mortar box
Mortar hoe
Mortar mixer
Mortar pans and stands
Portable circular saw
Portable concrete saw
Power activated nailer
Power compactor

Power elevator
Power float/troweler
Power screed
Rebar bender/cutter
Reciprocating saw
Rope and pulley
Rotary hammer
Round point shovel
Scaffolding
Square point shovel
Tuckpointer's grinder
Water hose
Wood mortar boards
Wooden body wheelbarrow

Job Practice Contents

IV. BLOCK MASONRY

V. STONE MASONRY

VI. CONCRETE WORK

Job Practice 1
Identifying Common Masonry Materials

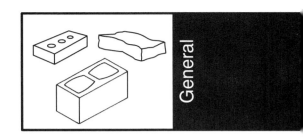

Name_____

Date_____

Instructor _____

Period _____

Objective

After completing this job you will be able to identify common masonry materials as to their basic group and name identification.

Equipment

To complete this job you will need the following tools and materials:

❖ Writing instrument (pencil)

❖ Flexible tape or folding rule (measuring device)

❖ Textbook for reference

❖ 16 common masonry materials (selected by instructor)

Recommended Procedure

Study the appropriate sections in Chapter 5 (Clay Masonry Materials), Chapter 6 (Concrete Masonry Units), and Chapter 7 (Stone) before starting this job.

1. Place each masonry material in one of the following groups:
   A. Clay brick
   B. Clay tile
   C. Concrete masonry unit
   D. Sand lime brick
   E. Glass block
   F. Natural stone
   G. Manufactured stone

Completed ❑

2. Write the accepted name and category (see list in Number 1) of each masonry unit in the spaces below. Use your rule or tape to measure units to help you determine their identification. Refer to your text for sizes and names.

A. _____

B. _____

C. _____

D. _____

E. _____

F. _____

G. _____

H. _____

I. _____

J. _____

K. _____

L. _____

M. _____

N. _____

O. _____

P. _____   Completed ☐

Instructor's Initials: _____

Date: _____

Job Practice 1 Review

After completing this job successfully, identify the following masonry materials correctly:

1. Category: _____

   Name: _____

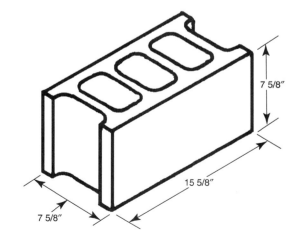

7 5/8"

15 5/8"

7 5/8"

Name_____

2. Category: _____
   Name:_____

12 × 12   12 × 12

3. Category: _____
   Name:_____

2 1/4″
8″
3 3/4″

4. Category: _____
   Name:_____

2 3/4″
8″
3 3/4″

5. Category: _____
   Name:_____

6″   12″   8″   12″

6. Category: _____
   Name:_____

7. Category: _____

   Name: _____

8. Category: _____

   Name: _____

9. Category: _____

   Name: _____

10. Category: _____

    Name: _____

Score: _____

Job Practice **2**
Identifying Types of Clay Bricks

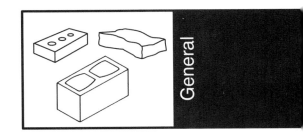

Name_____

Date_____

Instructor _____

Period _____

Objective

After completing this job you will be able to identify a wide variety of types of clay brick.

Equipment

To complete this job you will need the following tools and materials:

- ❖ Writing instrument (pencil)
- ❖ Flexible tape or folding rule (measuring device)
- ❖ Textbook for reference
- ❖ 16 common types of clay brick (selected by instructor)

Recommended Procedure

Study the appropriate section in Chapter 5 (Clay Masonry Materials) before starting this job.

1. Place each clay masonry unit in one of the following groups:
   - A. Building brick
   - B. Facing brick
   - C. Hollow brick
   - D. Paving brick
   - E. Ceramic glazed brick
   - F. Thin brick veneer units
   - G. Sewer or manhole brick

Completed ☐

2. Write the accepted name and category (see list in Number 1) of each clay masonry unit in the spaces below. Use your rule or tape to measure the brick to help you determine their identification. Refer to your text for sizes and names.

A. _____

B. _____

C. _____

D. _____

E. _____

F. _____

G. _____

H. _____

I. _____

J. _____

K. _____

L. _____

M. _____

N. _____

O. _____

P. _____   Completed ☐

Instructor's Initials:_____

Date: _____

Job Practice 2 Review

After completing this job successfully, identify the following clay masonry materials correctly. Use these group names: building brick, facing brick, hollow brick, paving brick, ceramic glazed brick, thin brick veneer, and sewer or manhole brick.

1. _____

Name_____

2. _____

3. _____

4. _____

5. _____

6. _____

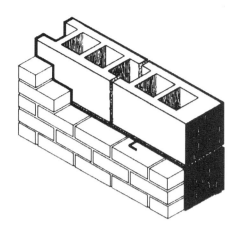

7. _____

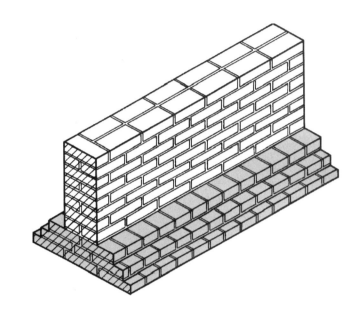

Score: _____

Job Practice 3
Arranging Brick in the Five Basic Structural Bonds

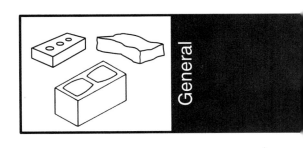

Name_____

Date_____

Instructor _____

Period _____

Objective

After completing this job you will be able to arrange bricks in each of the five basic structural bonds—Running, Common, Flemish, English, and Stack.

Equipment

To complete this job you will need the following tools and materials:

- ❖ Forty-five common bricks
- ❖ Thirty-six half bricks (snap headers)
- ❖ Eight three-quarter closures
- ❖ Eight quarter brick closures

Recommended Procedure

Study the appropriate section in Chapter 5 (Clay Masonry Materials) before starting this job.

1. Arrange the bricks in a single wythe (dry bond) in running bond nine courses high. See Illustration 3-1.

 Warning! Lay the bricks on a flat smooth surface as though the wall were horizontal rather than vertical. Nine courses of bricks might fall over and injure someone.

Completed ❑

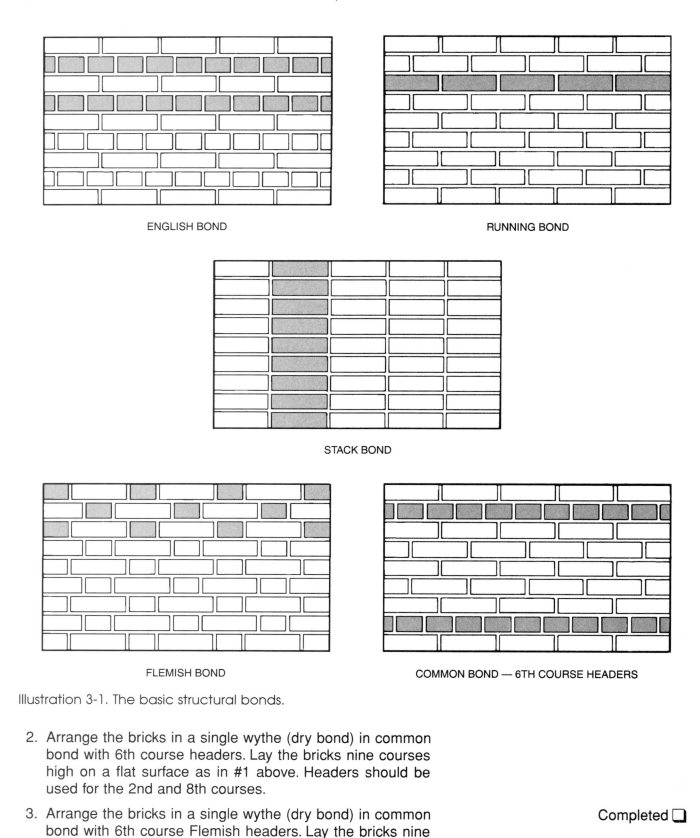

ENGLISH BOND

RUNNING BOND

STACK BOND

FLEMISH BOND

COMMON BOND — 6TH COURSE HEADERS

Illustration 3-1. The basic structural bonds.

2. Arrange the bricks in a single wythe (dry bond) in common bond with 6th course headers. Lay the bricks nine courses high on a flat surface as in #1 above. Headers should be used for the 2nd and 8th courses.

3. Arrange the bricks in a single wythe (dry bond) in common bond with 6th course Flemish headers. Lay the bricks nine courses high.

Completed ❑

Completed ❑

Name_____

4. Arrange the bricks in a single wythe (dry bond) in Flemish bond. Lay the bricks nine courses high.

Completed ❑

5. Arrange the bricks in a single wythe (dry bond) in English bond. Lay the bricks nine courses high.

Completed ❑

6. Arrange the bricks in a single wythe (dry bond) in Stack bond. Lay the bricks nine courses high.

Completed ❑

Instructor's Initials:_____

Date: _____

Job Practice 3 Review

After completing this job successfully, identify the following structural bonds correctly. The types are running, common, Flemish, English, and stack.

1. _____

2. _____

3. _____

4. _____

5. _____

Score: _____

Job Practice 4
Identifying Common Concrete Masonry Units

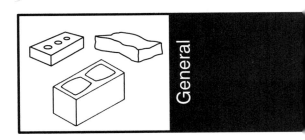

Name_____

Date_____

Instructor _____

Period _____

Objective

After completing this job you will be able to identify common concrete masonry units as to their basic group and name.

Equipment

To complete this job you will need the following tools and materials:

❖ Writing instrument (pencil)

❖ Flexible tape or folding rule (measuring device)

❖ Textbook for reference

❖ 16 common types of concrete masonry units (selected by instructor)

Recommended Procedure

Study the appropriate section in Chapter 6 (Concrete Masonry Units) before starting this job.

1. Place each concrete masonry unit in one of the following groups:
   A. Concrete brick
   B. Loadbearing concrete block
   C. Nonloadbearing concrete block
   D. Calcium silicate face brick
   E. Prefaced concrete units
   F. Units for catch basins and manholes

Completed ☐

2. Write the accepted name and category (see list in Number 1) of each concrete masonry unit in the spaces below. Use your rule to measure the units to help you determine their identification. Refer to your text for sizes and names.

A. _____

B. _____

C. _____

D. _____

E. _____

F. _____

G. _____

H. _____

I. _____

J. _____

K. _____

L. _____

M. _____

N. _____

O. _____

P. _____   Completed ❑

Instructor's Initials:_____

Date: _____

Job Practice 4 Review

After completing this job successfully, identify the following concrete masonry units correctly. The types possible are: concrete brick, loadbearing concrete block, nonloadbearing concrete block, calcium silicate face brick, prefaced concrete units, and units for catch basins and manholes.

1. _____

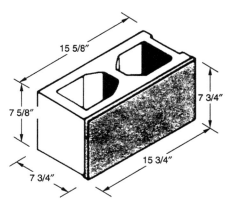

Name_____

2.   _____

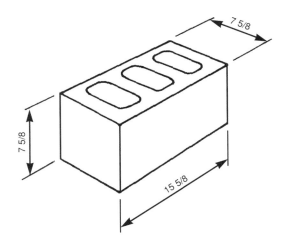

3.   _____

4. _____

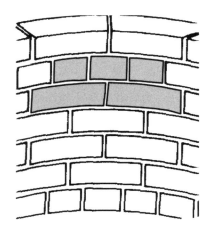

5. _____

Score: _____

Job Practice **5**
Identifying Common Concrete Block Shapes by Name

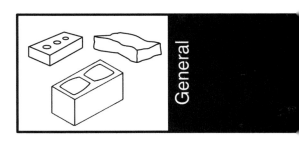

Name_____

Date_____

Instructor _____

Period _____

Objective

After completing this job you will be able to identify common concrete block shapes by name.

Equipment

To complete this job you will need the following tools and materials:

- ❖ Writing instrument (pencil)
- ❖ Flexible tape or folding rule (measuring device)
- ❖ Textbook for reference
- ❖ Twelve common types of concrete masonry units (selected by instructor). Each unit should be identified with a number.

Recommended Procedure

Study the appropriate section in Chapter 6 (Concrete Masonry Units) before starting this job.

1. Examine each concrete masonry unit to determine charac-teristics that help to identify it as to its type (name). For example, does it have cells? What are its dimensions? Does it have a unique shape? Where might it be used in con-struction? How much does it weigh?

Completed ☐

2. Record the name of each concrete masonry unit beside its identification number in the spaces below. Example: Jamb block, Corner block, Stretcher. See the list of names in Illustration 5-1 below.

A. _____

B. _____

C. _____

D. _____

E. _____

F. _____

G. _____

H. _____

I. _____

J. _____

K. _____

L. _____

M. _____

Completed ☐

Stretcher Block	Lintel Block	Depressed-Face Unit
Corner Block	Solid Block	Screen Block
Double Corner Block	Slab or Partition Block	Preface Unit
Sash Block	Half-Hi Full Length Block	Lightweight Stretcher
Sash Half Block		Sound Block
Jamb Block	Half-Hi Half Length Block	Slump Block
Jamb Half Block	Soffit Floor Block	Ground Face Unit
Single Bull Nose Block	Insulating Block	Control Joint Block
Double Bull Nose Block	Ribbed Unit	Solid Top Block
Double Bull Nose Face Block	Fluted Unit	Channel Block
1/4 Block	Stri-Face Unit	One-Piece Chimney Block
3/4 Block	Split-Fluted Unit	Pilaster Block
Full Cut Out Header Block	Split-Face Unit	Standard Wall Two-Core Block
Half Cut Out Header Block	Sculptured-Face Unit	Glazed Block
	Offset-Face Unit	

Illustration 5-1. Names of concrete masonry units.

Instructor's Initials:_____

Date: _____

Name_____

Job Practice 5 Review ▬▬▬▬▬▬▬▬▬▬

After completing this job successfully, identify the common concrete block shapes below by name.

1. _____

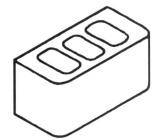

2. _____

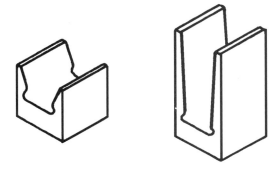

3. _____

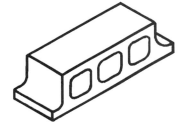

4. _____

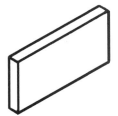

5. _____

6. _____

7. _____

8. _____

Score: _____

Job Practice 6
Identifying Common Building Stone Samples

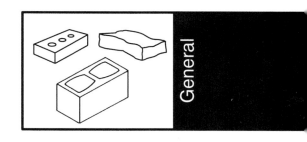

Name_____

Date_____

Instructor _____

Period _____

Objective

After completing this job you will be able to identify common building stones as to their basic group and name.

Equipment

To complete this job you will need the following tools and materials:

❖ Writing instrument (pencil)

❖ Textbook for reference

❖ Ten common types of building stone (selected by instructor). Each sample will be identified with a number.

Recommended Procedure

Study the appropriate section in Chapter 7 (Stone) before starting this job.

1. Identify each sample in terms of its group: Igneous (volcanic), Sedimentary, or Metamorphic. Write the group name beside its identification number in the space provided following step #2.

Completed ❑

2. Identify the name of each sample and record the name beside its identification number and group name below. Refer to the text for help in identifying the samples. The following stone types are typical: Granite, Traprock, Sandstone, Limestone, Marble, Slate, Schist, Gneiss, Quartzite.

A _____

B. _____

C. _____

D. _____

E. _____

F. _____

G. _____

H. _____

I. _____

J. _____   Completed ☐

Instructor's Initials:_____

Date: _____

Job Practice 6 Review

After completing this job successfully, identify the following types of building stone correctly.

1. _____

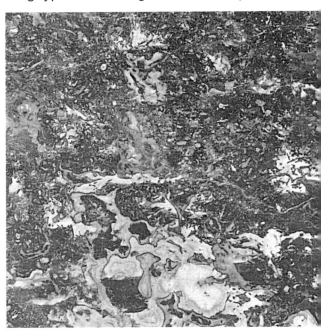

Name_____

2. _____

3. _____

4. _____

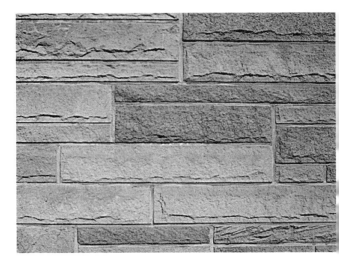

Score: _____

Job Practice 7
Measuring Mortar Materials and Mixing Mortar

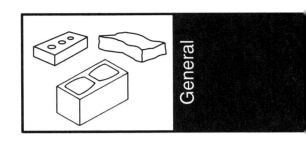

General

Name_____

Date_____

Instructor _____

Period _____

Objective

After completing this job you will be able to measure mortar materials using recommended practices and mix mortar to the proper consistency.

Equipment

To complete this job you will need the following tools and materials:

❖ Bag of masonry cement or Type I Portland cement and Type S hydrated lime

❖ Masonry sand

❖ Water suitable for mixing mortar

❖ One cubic foot measuring box

❖ Bucket or pail for measuring water

❖ Mixing box

❖ Mortar hoe

❖ Eye and hand protection

❖ Mason's trowel

Recommended Procedure

Study the appropriate section in Chapter 8 (Mortar and Grout) before starting this job.

1. Collect the materials and tools needed to measure and mix mortar materials. Arrange the items in such a way that they are convenient to the work area.   Completed ❑

2. Add one cubic foot of sand to the mixing box. Use the one cubic foot measuring box to measure the sand.   Completed ❑

3. Add 1/3 cubic foot of masonry cement to the mixing box. Use the one cubic foot measuring box to measure the masonry cement. Note: If Portland cement and lime are used instead of masonry cement, use 1/3 cubic foot of cement and 1/12 cubic foot of lime. Wear eye protection.   Completed ❑

4. Mix the sand and cement together with the mortar hoe. These ingredients must be mixed thoroughly before adding water. Work the materials from one end of the box to the other several times.   Completed ❑

5. Add two-thirds to three-fourths of the water and mix with the mortar hoe until the batch is uniformly wet. Experience will help you determine about how much water to add. (There are 8.33 pounds per gallon of water.) The general guideline is to add the maximum amount of water consistent with workability to provide maximum tensile bond strength. Your instructor will help you estimate how much water will be needed for this batch.   Completed ❑

6. Add more water to the batch and mix until the ingredients are thoroughly mixed and the batch is smooth and creamy. Check to see if the mortar has the right plasticity and adhesiveness by cutting ridges with the trowel or spade. Well-mixed mortar will form sharp ridges.   Completed ❑

7. Dispose of the mortar as per your instructor's directions. Clean all tools and return all the unused materials to their proper storage place.   Completed ❑

Instructor's Initials:_____

Date: _____

Job Practice 7 Review

After completing the job successfully, answer the following questions correctly:

1. Since mortar can be mixed using a variety of mix proportions, why is it so important that the ingredients be measured exactly the same each time?_____

_____

_____

_____

2. Why not add all of the water to the mix instead of adding about two-thirds to three-fourths of it after the cement and sand have been mixed? _____

_____

_____

_____

Name_____

3. How do you know when the mortar was mixed to just the right consistency?_____

_____

_____

_____

4. Why will mortar stick to the trowel, but concrete won't?_____

_____

_____

5. What is the difference between masonry cement and Portland cement? _____

_____

_____

_____

Score: _____

Job Practice **8**
Identifying Common Anchors, Ties, and Joint Reinforcement

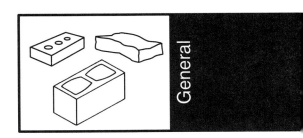

General

Name_____

Date_____

Instructor _____

Period _____

Objective

After completing this job you will be able to identify common anchors, ties, and joint reinforcement used in concrete and masonry construction.

Equipment

To complete this job you will need the following tools and materials:

❖ Writing instrument (pencil)

❖ Textbook for reference

❖ 12 common anchors, ties, and joint reinforcement used in concrete and masonry construction (selected by instructor). Each item should be identified with a number.

Recommended Procedure

Study the appropriate section in Chapter 9 (Anchors, Ties, and Joint Reinforcement) before starting this job.

1. Identify each sample as an anchor, tie, or joint reinforcement. Write the name of the type beside the identification number in the space following step 2 on the following page.

Completed ❑

2. Identify the name of each sample and record the name beside its identification number and group name below. Refer to the text for help in identifying each sample. The following names are typical:

Rectangular ties	Ladder type reinforcement
Z ties	Truss type reinforcement
Corrugated ties	Tab type reinforcement
Adjustable unit ties	Expansion bolts
Adjustable assemblies	Epoxy adhesive bolts
Reinforcing bar	Dovetail anchor
"J" anchor bolt	"L" anchor bolt
Anchor strap	Hardware cloth
Through rods	Power-driven pin

A. _____

B. _____

C. _____

D. _____

E. _____

F. _____

G. _____

H. _____

I. _____

J. _____

K. _____

L. _____   Completed ☐

Instructor's Initials:_____

Date: _____

Job Practice 8 Review

After completing this job successfully, answer the following questions correctly:

1. Why are anchor bolts used in masonry construction? _____

_____

_____

_____

Name_____

2. Why does the embedded end of most anchor bolts have a head, plate, or bent angle?_____

_____

_____

3. How is joint reinforcement used in brick or block masonry? _____

_____

_____

_____

4. In what type of application (wall) are corrugated fasteners generally used?_____

_____

_____

_____

5. How does an expansion bolt develop its holding power?_____

_____

_____

_____

6. When might an adjustable assembly be used? _____

_____

_____

Score: _____

Job Practice 9

Loading the Trowel and Spreading a Mortar Bed for Brick and Block

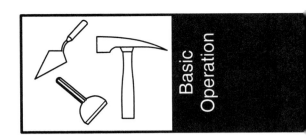

Name_____

Date_____

Instructor _____

Period _____

Objective

After completing this job you will be able to spread a mortar bed for clay brick and concrete block using proper technique.

Equipment

To complete this job you will need the following tools and materials:

❖ Standard mason's trowel

❖ Four clay bricks

❖ Two concrete blocks

❖ Mortar

❖ Mortar board

❖ Eye and hand protection

Recommended Procedure

Study the appropriate section in Chapter 2 (Safety) before starting this job.

1. Review safety precautions when using cementitious materials.

Completed ☐

2. Collect the tools and materials needed for this job and arrange a work area that is convenient and functional.

Completed ☐

3. Mix a batch of mortar following the procedure described in Job Practice 7. Place a generous amount of mortar on your mortar board and work it into a neat pile.

Completed ☐

4. Practice loading the trowel by following these steps or other procedure that feels natural to you:

   A. Grasp the trowel in your right hand if you are right-handed, with the thumb on top of the ferrule and the fingers under the handle.

   B. Work the mortar into a pile into the center of the mortar board.

   C. Smooth off a place with a backhand stroke.

   D. Cut a small amount from the larger pile with a pulling action.

   E. Scoop up the small pile with a quick movement of the trowel. Illustration 9-1 shows the loaded trowel.   Completed ❑

Illustration 9-1. Trowel loaded and ready.

5. Lay down a mortar bed for a course of bricks using a quick turn of the wrist toward the body and a backward movement of the arm. As the trowel is nearly empty, tip the trowel blade even more to help the remaining mortar slide off.   Completed ❑

6. Furrow the mortar bed with the point of the trowel. This helps to form a uniform bed for solid masonry units. See Illustration 9-2.   Completed ❑

Name_____

Illustration 9-2. Furrowing the first course to form a uniform bed.

7. Press several bricks into the bed of mortar. Do not apply head joints since that procedure has not yet been discussed. Note the pressure needed to set the bricks.

Completed ❑

8. Practice the procedure for loading the trowel and spreading a bed of mortar for bricks until it feels comfortable and you can judge the right amount of mortar needed.

Completed ❑

9. Repeat the process described above, but this time prepare a bed for concrete blocks. The same approach is used, but a wider bed is needed.

Completed ❑

10. Using both hands, grasp two cell webs and place a concrete block on the mortar bed, pressing it lightly into place. This process will be practiced in more detail later. (The thicker edge of the shell is on top to provide a wider mortar bed for the next course.)

Completed ❑

11. Practice laying down a mortar bed for concrete blocks until you are confident of the process.

Completed ❑

12. Clean the mortar from the masonry units, mortar board, work surface, and tools. Return tools and materials to their proper places and dispose of the mortar as directed by your instructor.

Completed ❑

 Warning! Contact with wet (plastic) concrete, cement, mortar, grout, or cement mixtures can cause skin irritation, severe chemical burns, or serious eye damage. Wear waterproof gloves, a long-sleeved shirt, full-length trousers, and proper eye protection when working with these materials. Wash wet mortar from your skin immediately. Flush your eyes with clear water immediately upon contact. Seek medical attention if you experience a reaction to contact with these materials.

Instructor's Initials:_____

Date: _____

Job Practice 9 Review ▬▬▬▬▬▬▬▬▬▬▬▬

After completing this job successfully, answer the following questions correctly:

1. Construction is a dangerous business, therefore, safety is a major consideration on the job. Describe a properly dressed worker in the masonry trades. _____

   _____

   _____

   _____

2. Describe the recommended method of holding the mason's trowel. _____

   _____

   _____

   _____

3. What did you find was the most difficult part in loading the trowel and spreading a bed of mortar?

   _____

   _____

4. Knowing when and just how much to temper (add water) your mortar is an important skill that every mason must learn. Did you have to temper your mortar? How did you know that it needed more water? _____

   _____

   _____

   _____

5. How long do you generally have to use up a batch of mortar before it begins to set? _____

Score: _____

Job Practice **10**
Forming a Head Joint on Brick and Block

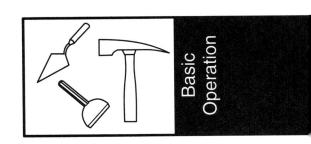

Name_____

Date_____

Instructor _____

Period _____

Objective

After completing this job you will be able to form a head joint on brick and block using proper technique.

Equipment

To complete this job you will need the following tools and materials:

- ❖ Standard mason's trowel
- ❖ Six clay bricks
- ❖ Four concrete blocks
- ❖ Mortar
- ❖ Mortar board
- ❖ Eye and hand protection

Recommended Procedure

Study the appropriate sections in Chapter 2 (Safety), Chapter 10 (Laying Brick), and Chapter 11 (Laying Block) before starting this job.

1. Review safety precautions when using cementitious materials.   Completed ❑

2. Collect the tools and materials needed for this job and arrange a work area that is convenient and functional.   Completed ❑

3. Mix a batch of mortar following the procedure described in Job Practice 7. Place a generous amount of mortar on your mortar board and work it into a neat pile.   Completed ❑

4. Lay down a mortar bed for a course six bricks long. Furrow the mortar bed so that it is ready to receive the base course of bricks. Place the first brick on the bed without a head joint.   Completed ❑

5. Pick up a brick in your left hand (if you are right handed) holding it about midpoint across the brick. Load your trowel with the other hand and apply mortar to the end of the brick with a swiping or throwing action across the end of the brick. This motion should attach the mortar to the brick and form it into a wedge shape. See Illustration 10-1.   Completed ❑

Illustration 10-1. Forming a head joint on a brick.

6. Bevel the mortar slightly at the corners with the trowel. Press the brick into the mortar bed and against the brick already in place. Some mortar should squeeze out between the bricks.   Completed ❑

7. Repeat the process several times to develop the proper hand/wrist action. The purpose of this job is to learn how to apply head joints, not lay brick.   Completed ❑

8. Remove the brick and mortar. Clean the mortar off the brick and work surface for the next operation.   Completed ❑

9. Lay down a mortar bed for a course of concrete block using the procedure practiced in Job Practice 9.   Completed ❑

10. Place one concrete block on the mortar bed and press it into place. Do not apply a head joint to the block.   Completed ❑

11. Set several blocks on end so that the ears face up to receive the mortar. Scoop some mortar on the trowel, but do not fully load it. Use a downward swiping action to apply the mortar to the ears of the blocks.   Completed ❑

12. Next, press down the mortar on the inside of each ear of the block to attach it to the block. If the mortar is not attached sufficiently, it will fall off when the block is lifted and turned for placement in the wall.   Completed ❑

Name_____

13. Lift the block with both hands and place on the mortar bed next to the first block. Press down and against the other block to form a good watertight joint. Mortar should squeeze out.

Completed ❏

14. Practice applying head joints to blocks several times to develop the proper action and to apply the right amount of mortar to the block.

Completed ❏

15. Clean the mortar from the masonry units, mortar board, work surface, and tools. Return the tools and materials to their proper places and dispose of the mortar as directed by your instructor.

Completed ❏

Instructor's Initials:_____

Date: _____

Job Practice 10 Review ▬▬▬▬▬▬▬▬▬▬▬▬▬▬

After completing this job successfully, answer the following questions correctly:

1. One of the problems that student masons have is keeping mortar on the brick or block as they move it toward its destination. What do you think might be the cause for this?_____

_____

_____

_____

2. When forming head joints, how did you know that you had applied enough mortar to form a full head joint? _____

_____

_____

_____

3. If a little mortar is good, then why not apply lots to form the head joint?_____

_____

_____

4. Did you load your trowel with more or less mortar when forming head joints on block than when forming head joints on brick? _____

_____

5. If some of the mortar falls off when placing a brick or block, should you go ahead and place it and then fill the joint?_____

_____

Score: _____

Job Practice 11
Cutting Bricks with the Brick Hammer

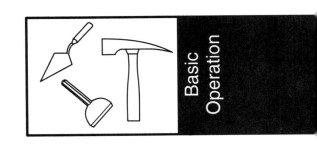

Name_____

Date_____

Instructor _____

Period _____

Objective

After completing this job you will be able to cut bricks with a brick hammer using proper technique.

Equipment

To complete this job you will need the following tools and materials:

❖ Brick hammer

❖ Several bricks

❖ Eye and hand protection

Recommended Procedure

Study the appropriate section in Chapter 10 (Laying Brick) before starting this job.

1. The method of cutting bricks most frequently used by masons is the brick hammer. Begin by holding the brick in one hand, keeping the fingers away from the side where the cutting will take place. With the other hand, strike the brick with light blows with the blade edge of the brick hammer along the line where the cut is planned.

   Completed ❑

2. Turn the brick over to the adjacent edge and continue the cut along that side.

   Completed ❑

3. Repeat the process until all sides have been scored. Then strike the face of the brick with a sharp blow with the hammer. The brick should break along the scored lines. Be sure to wear safety glasses.

   Completed ❑

4. Repeat the procedure several times to develop the proper technique.

   Completed ❑

Instructor's Initials:_____

Date: _____

Job Practice 11 Review ▬▬▬▬▬▬▬▬▬▬▬▬▬▬▬▬▬

You should be able to answer the following questions correctly after completing this job successfully:

1. When cutting bricks, masons use the brick hammer the most. Why do you think this is true? _____

   _____

   _____

2. As a novice brick mason, why do you think that it is a good idea to draw a line on the brick where you wish to break it with the brick hammer? _____

   _____

   _____

3. Why do you need to cut a groove along all sides of the brick before striking the brick to break it?

   _____

   _____

4. When you have scored the brick on all sides, which part of the brick hammer do you use to strike the brick? _____

   _____

5. What is the most important piece of safety equipment you should be wearing when cutting bricks with a brick hammer? _____

   _____

Score: _____

Job Practice 12
Cutting Bricks with the Brick Set Chisel

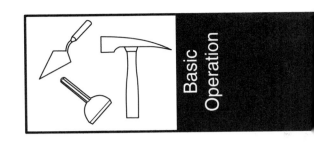

Name_____

Date_____

Instructor _____

Period _____

Objective

After completing this job you will be able to cut bricks with a brick set chisel using proper technique.

Equipment

To complete this job you will need the following tools and materials:

❖ Brick hammer

❖ Brick set chisel

❖ Several bricks

❖ Eye and hand protection

Recommended Procedure

Study the appropriate section in Chapter 10 (Laying Brick) before starting this job.

1. When a more accurate, straight cut is needed, the brick set chisel may be used. First, mark the brick with a pencil or other marking device where the cut is to be made.

   Completed ❑

2. Place the brick on a soft surface such as soil or board. Hold the chisel end of the brick set vertically with the flat side of the blade facing the direction of the finished cut.

   Completed ❑

3. Strike the brick set sharply with the brick hammer. The resulting cut should be relatively smooth and not require additional chipping before use in the wall. Be sure to wear safety glasses.

   Completed ❑

4. Repeat the procedure several times to develop the proper technique.

   Completed ❑

Instructor's Initials:_____

Date: _____

Job Practice 12 Review ▬▬▬▬▬▬▬▬▬▬

After completing this job successfully, answer the following questions correctly:

1. Why would you use the brick set chisel to cut a brick rather than the brick hammer? _____

   _____

   _____

2. Why shouldn't you place the brick on a hard surface such as a slab of concrete to cut it with the brick set chisel?_____

   _____

   _____

3. Which side of the chisel should be facing the direction of the finished cut and why? _____

   _____

   _____

4. Why is it necessary to keep the brick set chisel sharp? _____

   _____

   _____

5. What should you do if a piece of brick somehow gets past your safety glasses and lodges in your eye? _____

   _____

   _____

Score: _____

Job Practice 13
Cutting Bricks with the Mason's Trowel

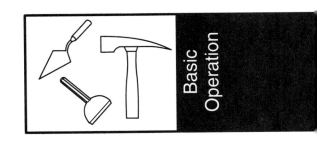

Basic Operation

Name_____

Date_____

Instructor_____

Period _____

Objective

After completing this job you will be able to cut bricks with a brick mason's trowel using proper technique.

Equipment

To complete this job you will need the following tools and materials:

- ❖ Standard mason's trowel
- ❖ Several bricks
- ❖ Eye and hand protection

Recommended Procedure

Study the appropriate section in Chapter 10 (Laying Brick) before starting this job.

1. The mason's trowel can be used to cut softer bricks, but is not recommended for most cutting, especially hard bricks. When cutting a brick with the trowel, hold the brick in one hand, keeping the fingers away from the side where the cutting is to be done.

Completed ❑

 Warning! Be sure you are wearing safety glasses during the following procedure.

2. Hold the brick down away from the face. Strike the brick with the edge of the trowel using a quick, sharp blow at the spot where the cut (break) is intended.

Completed ❑

3. Repeat the process several times to develop the technique.

Completed ❑

4. Clean up the pieces and return all tools and materials to their proper place.

Completed ❑

Instructor's Initials:_____

Date: _____

Job Practice 13 Review

After completing this job successfully, answer the following questions correctly:

1. Why shouldn't you cut hard brick with the mason's trowel? _____

_____

_____

2. Why do some masons insist on cutting hard brick with the trowel?_____

_____

_____

3. Why is cutting bricks with the trowel basically unsafe? _____

_____

_____

4. What type of masonry unit can be cut with a brick mason's trowel? _____

_____

Score: _____

Job Practice **14**
Cutting Bricks with the Masonry Saw

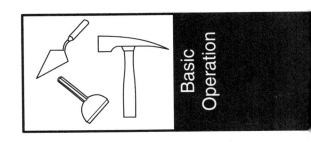

Basic Operation

Name_____

Date_____

Instructor _____

Period _____

Objective

After completing this job you will be able to cut bricks with a masonry saw using proper technique.

Equipment

To complete this job you will need the following tools and materials:

❖ Power masonry saw

❖ Several bricks

❖ Eye and hand protection

Recommended Procedure

Study the appropriate section in Chapter 10 (Laying Brick) before starting this job.

1. When an exact, smooth cut is required, a power masonry saw may be used. This process is slower, but produces the highest quality cut. Ask your instructor to demonstrate the proper and safe use of the masonry saw.

Completed ❑

 Warning! Be sure you are wearing safety glasses during the following procedure.

2. Hold the brick firmly against the fence and move the saw slowly through the cut. Do not rush the cut or let the brick move while making the cut.

Completed ❑

3. Move the saw back to its original position before removing the pieces.

Completed ❑

4. Repeat the process several times to develop confidence in
   using this dangerous machine.   Completed ☐

Trade Tip. Use this procedure to cut concrete blocks using the masonry saw.

Instructor's Initials:_____

Date: _____

Job Practice 14 Review ▬▬▬▬▬▬▬▬▬▬▬▬▬

After completing this job successfully, answer the following questions correctly:

1. When would you elect to use a masonry saw to cut a brick rather than the brick hammer, trowel, or
   brick set chisel? _____

   _____

2. How does the blade on a masonry saw cut the brick?_____

   _____

   _____

3. What one piece of safety equipment is absolutely required when operating the masonry saw?

   _____

   _____

4. How could you tell if you were moving the saw through the cut at too high a rate of speed?_____

   _____

   _____

5. What would you look for in a routine examination of the masonry saw before using it? _____

   _____

   _____

Score: _____

Job Practice 15

Cutting Concrete Blocks with a Brick Hammer and Blocking Chisel

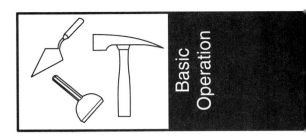

Basic Operation

Name_____

Date_____

Instructor _____

Period _____

Objective

After completing this job you will be able to cut concrete blocks with a mason's hammer and blocking chisel using proper technique.

Equipment

To complete this task you will need the following tools and materials:

❖ Brick hammer

❖ Blocking chisel

❖ Several concrete blocks

❖ Eye and hand protection

Recommended Procedure

Study the appropriate section in Chapter 11 (Laying Block) before starting this job.

1. Even though concrete blocks are available in half-length units as well as full-length units, it is sometimes necessary to cut blocks to fit. When using the blocking chisel, hold the beveled edge toward you so the piece to be cut off is facing away.

Completed ❑

  Warning! Be sure you are wearing safety glasses during the following procedure.

2. Place the chisel on the line where the cut is to be made. Strike the chisel with your brick hammer to score a line where the cut is to be made. See Illustration 15-1.

Completed ❑

Illustration 15-1. Cutting a concrete block with a blocking chisel and mason's hammer.

3. Turn the block over and cut the opposite side as before. When the cut is made, the block should break into two pieces.

Completed ☐

4. Practice cutting several blocks to determine the amount of face needed to make a quality cut.

Completed ☐

5. Clean up the pieces and return all tools and materials to their proper place.

Completed ☐

Instructor's Initials:_____

Date: _____

Job Practice 15 Review

After completing this job successfully, answer the following questions correctly:

1. What are the names of the tools used to cut concrete blocks by hand? _____

_____

2. What is the proper position of the blocking chisel when cutting a concrete block? _____

_____

3. What piece of safety equipment is absolutely essential when cutting concrete block with the blocking chisel?_____

_____

4. Why is it necessary to score both sides of the concrete block?_____

_____

_____

5. Can a concrete block be cut down through the web with the blocking chisel? _____

_____

Score: _____

Job Practice **16**
Using a Mason's Line

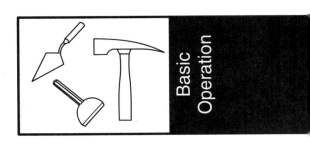

Name_____

Date_____

Instructor _____

Period _____

Objective

After completing this job you will be able to use a mason's line to establish the proper course height for a masonry wall.

Equipment

To complete this job you will need the following tools and materials:

❖ A length of mason's cord or line

❖ A mason's rule

❖ Plumb rule (level)

❖ Two leads or stacks of bricks or blocks to serve as lead (corners)

❖ Two line blocks (for bricks)

Recommended Procedure

Study the appropriate sections in Chapter 10 (Laying Brick) and Chapter 11 (Laying Block) before starting this job.

1. Select a partner to work with you on this job. Using a pair of leads (corners) of brick masonry, stretch out a length of mason's cord long enough to reach from the outside edge of one lead to the outside of the other.   Completed ☐

2. Ask your instructor to show you how to attach the cord to one of the line blocks. Have your partner hold the line block against the corner at the top edge of a course of masonry.   Completed ☐

3. Go to the other lead and place a line block at the same height. Attach the mason's cord to the line block. Pull the cord taut until all sag has been removed.   Completed ☐

4. Using the plumb rule (level), check the line to see if it is level.   Completed ☐

5. Using the mason's rule, measure the distance from the bed course of masonry to the location of the line block at each end. Compare the dimensions.   Completed ☐

6. Repeat the procedure, but reversing roles with your partner. Try the process two or three times until you can perform the task efficiently.   Completed ☐

7. Return the materials to their proper places.   Completed ☐

Trade Tip. This job can be repeated using adjustable line stretchers on concrete block leads.

Instructor's Initials:_____

Date: _____

Job Practice 16 Review

After completing this job successfully, answer the following questions correctly:

1. When should you use a mason's line instead of the plumb rule only? _____
   _____

2. How could you tell when the mason's line was tight enough?_____
   _____

3. What are the devices called that support each end of the mason's cord when laying a brick wall? How about concrete blocks?_____
   _____
   _____

4. How far away from the masonry units is the mason's cord positioned? _____
   _____

5. If the wall is very long, how is the mason's line supported in the middle to eliminate the sag? ____
   _____

Score:_____

Job Practice 17
Erecting Batter Boards

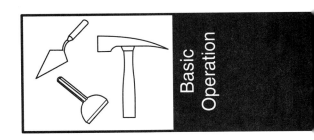

Name_____

Date_____

Instructor_____

Period_____

Objective

After completing this job you will be able to erect batter boards to preserve a foundation line using proper technique.

Equipment

To complete this job you will need the following tools and materials:

- ❖ Brick hammer
- ❖ A dozen 16 penny nails
- ❖ Four 2″ × 4″ × 2′ boards sharpened on one end
- ❖ Two 1″ × 4′ × 3′ boards
- ❖ Two 1″ × 1″ × 12″ stakes
- ❖ Length of mason's cord
- ❖ Plumb rule (level) or plumb bob
- ❖ 25′ flexible tape

Recommended Procedure

Study the appropriate section in Chapter 10 (Laying Brick) and Chapter 11 (Laying Block) before starting this job.

1. Batter boards are used to preserve the building line during excavation and construction. This job will establish a single building line. Drive the two 1″ × 1″ × 12″ stakes in the ground 12 ft. apart along an imaginary building line. See Illustration 17-1.

Completed ☐

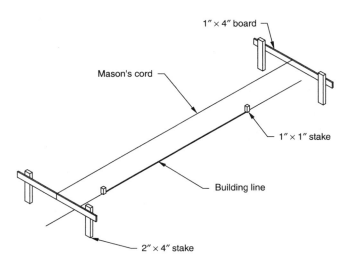

Illustration 17-1. Batter boards locating a building line.

2. Move out three feet beyond one stake, but in line with the building line. Drive two 2" × 4" × 2' stakes into the ground several inches so the widest side faces the building line stake. These stakes should be about 2' apart.   Completed ❑

3. Carefully nail a 1" × 4" × 3' board across the 2 × 4 stakes about 12" to 18" above the ground. This board should be relatively level.   Completed ❑

4. Move to the other end of the building line and repeat the operation.   Completed ❑

5. Stretch the cord across the horizontal board at either end so that it passes directly over the building line stakes. Tie it off using a slip knot. Use the level or plumb bob to be sure the line is over the stake.   Completed ❑

6. Mark the position of the cord on the horizontal board at each end so it can be removed and then positioned at the same location again later.   Completed ❑

7. Remove the cord, nails, and stakes and return all tools and materials to their assigned places.   Completed ❑

Instructor's Initials:_____

Date: _____

Name_____

Job Practice 17 Review ▬▬▬▬▬▬▬

After completing this job successfully, answer the following questions correctly:

1. What are batter boards used for?_____

_____

_____

2. What materials are generally used for the construction of batter boards?_____

_____

_____

3. Why is it necessary to mark the location of the line on the batter boards? _____

_____

_____

4. Is it absolutely necessary for the cross boards to be exactly level? _____

_____

5. Why are the batter boards positioned well away from the wall they locate? _____

_____

_____

6. Why is a slip knot or bow used to tie off the line on a batter board?_____

_____

_____

Score: _____

Job Practice 18
Laying Six Bricks on a Board

Name_____

Date_____

Instructor _____

Period _____

Objective

After completing this job you will be able to lay a course of bricks without a line using the proper tools and techniques.

Equipment

To complete this job you will need the following tools and materials:

- ❖ Mason's trowel
- ❖ Mortar board
- ❖ Mortar (provided by instructor)
- ❖ Six bricks
- ❖ Six foot board 2″ × 4″ (straight)
- ❖ Three concrete blocks
- ❖ Five gallon bucket with water
- ❖ Plumb rule (level)
- ❖ Mason's rule
- ❖ Brick hammer
- ❖ V-jointer or convex jointer
- ❖ Brush

Recommended Procedure

Study the appropriate section in Chapter 10 (Laying Brick) before starting this job.

1. Assemble the required tools and materials and set up a work space by placing the 2 × 4 board across two of the concrete blocks. This will raise the work space above the floor and make your work easier. The board should be close to level. See Illustration 18-1.

Completed ☐

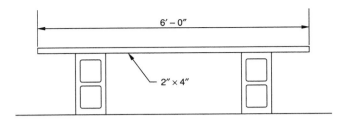

Illustration 18-1. The basic setup.

2. Stand your level in a cell hole in the remaining concrete block. Wet the mortar board and fill it with mortar. Place it on the five gallon bucket.

Completed ☐

3. Lay the six bricks on the board with a 3/8" space between them. Measure each one with your rule. Mark the joint locations on the side of the board.

Completed ☐

4. Spread mortar on the board to form the bed joint for six bricks. Furrow the mortar bed and cut off excess mortar along the edges of the board.

Completed ☐

5. Place the first brick on the mortar bed at the end on your left as you face the board. Press the brick into the mortar so that a bed joint 3/8" thick is formed. This equals No. 6 on the modular rule. Level the brick and be sure it is parallel to the board.

Completed ☐

6. Form a head joint on the second brick and put it in place next to the first brick. The head joint should also be 3/8" wide. Remove excess mortar.

Completed ☐

7. Lay the remaining bricks along the board and remove all excess mortar. Check the course to be sure it is level, straight, and plumb. See Illustration 18-2.

Completed ☐

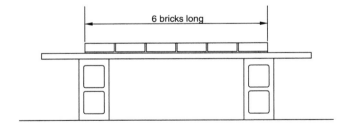

Illustration 18-2. Completed job.

Name_____

8. When the mortar is thumbprint hard, strike the joints with the V-jointer or convex jointer. Remove any tags with the trowel.   Completed ❏

9. Brush the brickwork to remove any excess mortar or dirt.   Completed ❏

10. Clean up the work area and tools and return the tools and materials to their assigned places.   Completed ❏

Instructor's Initials:_____

Date: _____

Job Practice 18 Review ▬▬▬▬▬▬▬▬▬▬▬▬

After completing this job successfully, answer the following questions correctly.

1. What was the function of the board in this job? _____
_____

2. Why was it necessary for the 2 × 4 board to be fairly close to level for this job? _____
_____
_____

3. Why was it recommended that you wet the mortar board before putting mortar on it?_____
_____
_____

4. What is the mortar joint thickness when a standard brick is used and laid to No. 6 on the modular rule? _____
_____
_____

5. How were the tags or fins removed after jointing the bricks?_____
_____
_____

6. After a brick was laid, which operation was then performed? _____
_____

Score: _____

Job Practice 19
Laying a Four Course, Single Wythe, Running Bond Lead

Brick Masonry

Name_____

Date_____

Instructor _____

Period _____

Objective

After completing this job you will be able to lay a simple four course, single wythe, running bond lead (corner) using proper technique.

Equipment

To complete this job you will need the following tools and materials:

- ❖ Mason's trowel
- ❖ Mortar board
- ❖ Mortar (provided by instructor)
- ❖ Fourteen bricks
- ❖ Five gallon bucket with water
- ❖ Plumb rule
- ❖ Modular rule
- ❖ Chalk line
- ❖ Brick hammer
- ❖ Convex jointer and sled runner
- ❖ Brush

Recommended Procedure

Study the appropriate section in Chapter 10 (Laying Brick) before starting this job.

1. The first step is to snap a chalk line where the face of the masonry wall is to be located along adjacent sides. Mark the actual head joints along the chalk line for proper placement of the masonry units. See Illustration 19-1.

Completed ☐

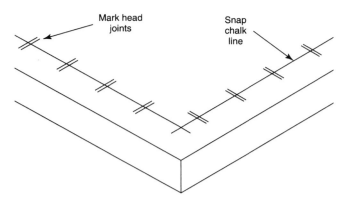

Illustration 19-1. Step #1.

2. Lay down a mortar bed and start the first course by laying the first unit from the corner. Level and plumb this brick. Remove excess mortar. Note, the placement marks for the head joints are visible even when the unit is in place. See Illustration 19-2.

Completed ☐

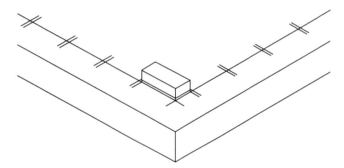

Illustration 19-2. Step #2.

3. Complete the first course along both legs of the lead. Check to be sure the bricks are spaced properly, straight, level, and plumb. Each leg should be about the same length. Leads are generally about seven or nine courses high, but a shorter lead may be used for practice, as in this case. See Illustration 19-3.

Completed ☐

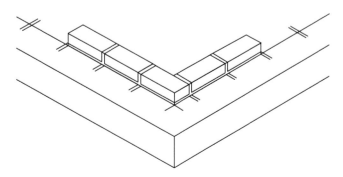

Illustration 19-3. Step #3.

Name_____

4. Lay up the second and third courses alternating the pattern of brick placement. Lay up the third course similar to the first course. See Illustration 19-4.

Completed ❏

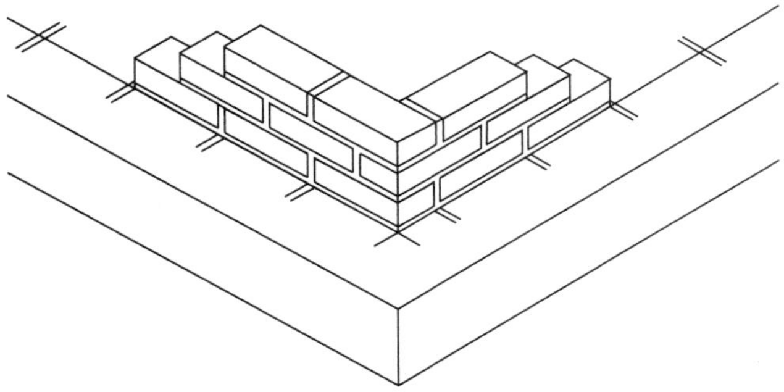

Illustration 19-4. Step #4.

5. Lay up the fourth course to complete the lead. Two bricks on the highest course of the lead will provide enough resistance to maintain a tight line. See Illustration 19-5.

Completed ❏

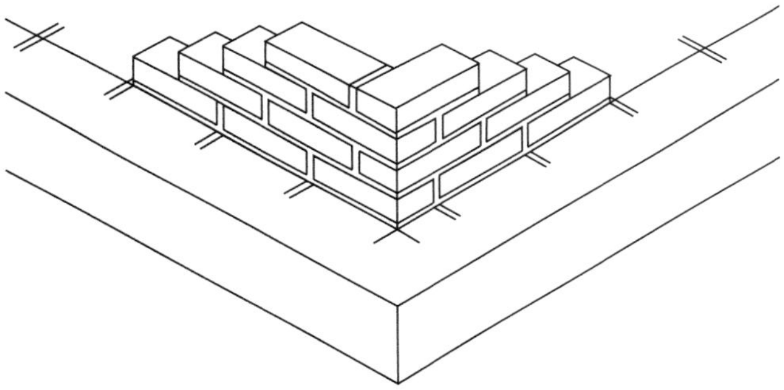

Illustration 19-5. Step #5.

6. Strike the joints when they are thumbprint hard. Remove any tags with the trowel and brush the wall to remove any mortar or dirt.

Completed ❏

7. Clean up the work area and return all tools and materials to their assigned places.

Completed ❏

Instructor's Initials:_____

Date: _____

Job Practice 19 Review ▬▬▬▬▬▬▬▬▬▬▬▬▬▬▬

After completing this job successfully, answer the following questions correctly:

1. What is a wythe? _____

_____

_____

2. What mason's tool is generally used to straightedge a course of brick? _____

_____

_____

3. Where is the first brick laid when building a lead? _____

_____

4. In a running bond, what courses are identical? _____

_____

_____

_____

5. Approximately how many courses high are most brick leads laid? _____

_____

6. Why are leads built? _____

_____

_____

7. If a wall were 10′ long and you did not want to build leads, what other approach could you use to support the mason's line?_____

_____

Score: _____

Job Practice 20
Laying a 4" Running Bond Wall with Leads

Brick Masonry

Name_____

Date_____

Instructor_____

Period _____

Objective

After completing this job you will be able to lay up a 4" running bond wall with leads using proper technique.

Equipment

To complete this job, you will need the following tools and materials:

- ❖ Mason's trowel
- ❖ Mortar board
- ❖ Mortar (provided by instructor)
- ❖ Supply of brick
- ❖ Five gallon bucket with water
- ❖ Plumb rule
- ❖ Mason's rule
- ❖ Chalk line
- ❖ Brick hammer
- ❖ Jointer

Recommended Procedure

Study the appropriate section in Chapter 10 (Laying Brick) before starting this job. Note: This job follows the pictorial sequence in your text. Refer to the photos when needed.

1. Arrange your work space for efficient work. The mortar board should be located in the center of the work space about 24" from the wall. Brick should be stacked on both sides of the board.

Completed ☐

2. Establish a wall line 6' long using a chalk line. Check each corner to be sure it is square. You can do this by measuring 6' along one side and 8' along the intersecting side. The diagonal distance between the points should be 10'. This procedure is known as the *6-8-10 rule*.

Completed ❑

3. Lay out a dry course of brick from corner to corner with uniform head joints. Mark the joints along the chalk line and then move the bricks aside.

Completed ❑

4. Spread the mortar on one side of the corner and furrow it. Lay the corner brick exactly on the point where the corner is located. It must be set level and square with the wall line.

Completed ❑

5. Lay the remaining four or five bricks of the lead corner. This is called "tailing out" the lead of the corner. After the bricks have been laid, level them with the plumb rule. Plumb the corner brick and then the tail end. Leveling is done on the outside and top edge of the brick.

Completed ❑

6. Line up the bricks between the two plumb points. Here the level is used as a straightedge and the bubbles are disregarded. Always follow this sequence when building a corner: level the unit, then plumb, and then line up.

Completed ❑

7. After one side of the corner has been laid and trued, start the other side of the corner. Spread the mortar and furrow it. Lay three or four bricks. Level, plumb, and line them up. Do not tap the level with the trowel or hammer. Use your hand. This time the corner brick does not require plumbing because it has already been plumbed.

Completed ❑

8. Lay the second course following the same sequence used for the first course. Check for proper height just after the course has been laid, but before the bricks have been leveled. If the brick are too high, tap them down as they are leveled. If they are too low, remove them and add more mortar before leveling.

Completed ❑

9. Repeat the sequence until the corner is built to a height of seven courses.

Completed ❑

10. Straightedge the rack of the lead to eliminate any wind, belly, or cave-in in the wall. This is accomplished by laying the level across the corner of each brick in the rack. The courses should line up.

Completed ❑

11. Lay the second corner of the wall following the same procedure used for the first.

Completed ❑

Name_____

12. Stretch the mason's line between the corners at the top of the first course. Use corner blocks and pull the line taut enough to remove any sag. Use the same amount of tension each time.   Completed ❑

13. Begin laying the wall from the lead toward the center, one course at a time. Each brick on the second course should be centered over the cross joint of the first course. Be sure the head joints are uniform so the last brick will fit properly. The line should be worked from both leads toward the center. Level, plumb, and line up each course as you lay it.   Completed ❑

14. Tool or strike the joints when the mortar is thumbprint hard. Use the sled jointer (long jointer) for the bed joints and then the short jointer for the vertical joints. Remove any tags with the trowel. You may want to use the jointers again to improve appearance.   Completed ❑

15. Brush the wall when the mortar is stiff enough. Brushing reduces the amount of cleaning required later.   Completed ❑

16. Lay the remaining courses in the same manner until the wall is completed to the required height of seven courses.   Completed ❑

17. Examine your work and note where it could be improved.   Completed ❑

18. Clean up the area and remove all mortar from your tools. Return materials and tools to their assigned places.   Completed ❑

Instructor's Initials:_____

Date: _____

Job Practice 20 Review

After completing this job successfully, answer the following questions correctly:

1. How is a corner squared using the 6-8-10 rule? _____

   _____

   _____

2. Why is a dry course of brick laid out before any mortar is used? _____

   _____

   _____

3. What is the proper order for the following operations when laying a course of bricks (line up the bricks, level the bricks, plumb the bricks)?_____

   _____

4. If a brick has too thick a mortar bed, how should you tap it down to the proper level?_____

_____

_____

5. What is the recommended procedure when a brick is too low (mortar bed too thin)? _____

_____

_____

6. How is the rack straightedged? _____

_____

_____

Score: _____

Job Practice **21**
Laying an 8" Common Bond, Double Wythe Brick Wall with Leads

Brick Masonry

Name_____

Date _____

Instructor _____

Period _____

Objective ▮▮▮▮▮▮▮▮▮▮▮▮▮▮▮▮▮▮▮▮▮▮▮▮▮

After completing this job you will be able to lay up an 8" American (common) bond, double wythe brick wall with leads using proper technique.

Equipment ▮▮▮▮▮▮▮▮▮▮▮▮▮▮▮▮▮▮▮▮▮▮▮▮▮

To complete this job you will need the following tools and materials:

- ❖ Mason's tools
- ❖ Mortar
- ❖ Supply of bricks

Recommended Procedure ▮▮▮▮▮▮▮▮▮▮▮▮▮▮▮

Study the appropriate section in Chapter 10 (Laying Brick) before starting this job.

1. Lay out the wall location as you did with the 4" wall in Job Practice 12. Locate a second line inside the first wall line equal to the length of the bricks being used (about 8). Your instructor will specify the length of the wall and lead tails.

   Completed ❑

2. Lay out the bond to eliminate cutting if possible. This is an important step. Mark the head joints to ensure proper and uniform placement.

   Completed ❑

3. Lay the corner bricks of the lead as shown in Illustration 21-1. Level, plumb, and square these bricks.

Completed ❑

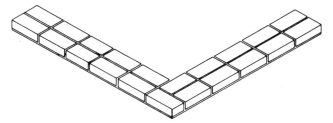

Illustration 21-1. First course.

4. Complete the first course following the pattern illustrated. Four or five stretchers should be sufficient. Check with your instructor.

Completed ❑

5. Study Illustration 21-2 before laying the second course of the lead. Notice that you will need 3 three-quarter closures, 1 bat (half brick), and 1 closure. In this job the header course is the second course, but it could begin wherever specified between five to seven courses of stretchers.

Completed ❑

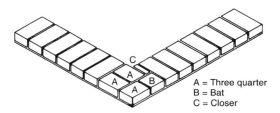

A = Three quarter
B = Bat
C = Closer

Illustration 21-2. Second course.

6. Lay the third through seventh courses of stretchers. Level, plumb, and line up each course as it is laid. See Illustration 21-3.

Completed ❑

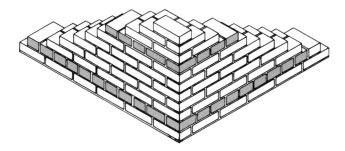

Illustration 21-3. Completed corner lead.

Name_____

7. Lay the eighth course of headers using the same pattern that was used in the second course. Notice how this configuration breaks the bond of the previous course.

Completed ❑

8. Finish laying the first corner as shown in Illustration 21-3. Strike all the joints as the mortar hardens to thumbprint hard. Remove the tags and brush the bricks. This is a good place to stop for the day.

Completed ❑

9. Lay the second corner using the same procedure that you followed in laying up the first corner. Refer to Illustrations 21-1, 21-2, and 21-3 again.

Completed ❑

10. Construct the first stretcher course of the wall by laying the outside first and then the inside. These should be laid from the leads toward the center. Level, plumb, and line up each course before beginning the next course. Refer to Illustration 21-4.

Completed ❑

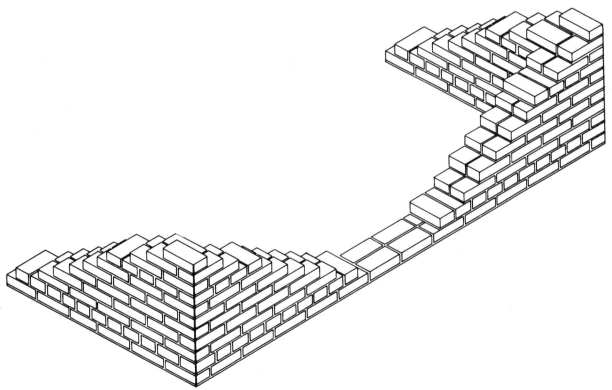

Illustration 21-4. Corner leads with first stretcher course.

11. Use a line to establish the height of the header course. Lay the header (second) course between the leads. Watch the width of your mortar joints to be sure the proper spacing is maintained. Level, plumb, and line up the header course.

Completed ❑

12. Lay the outside tier up to the next header course keeping it straight, level, and plumb. This is called "header high." Use the mason's line.

Completed ❑

13. Lay the inside tier up to the same height. Be careful to keep it level with the outside tier as it is laid up. This is important as you must have a level surface for the header course.

Completed ❑

14. Continue as before until the desired height is reached. Strike the joints and brush the wall at the proper time.

Completed ❑

15. Inspect your work, clean up the area, and return the unused materials and tools to their proper places.

Completed ❑

Instructor's Initials:_____

Date: _____

Job Practice 21 Review

After completing this job successfully, answer the following questions correctly:

1. How can a common bond wall be recognized? _____

_____

2. In addition to headers and stretchers, what other bricks were used to build this wall?_____

_____

_____

3. Once the first lead is built, what is the next operation in building an 8″ common bond, double wythe wall with leads? _____

_____

_____

4. How should the bricks be laid between the leads? _____

_____

_____

5. Should you wait until the wall is built before striking any joints? _____

_____

_____

6. What tool should be used to strike the bed joints on a brick wall? _____

_____

_____

Score: _____

Job Practice **22**
Laying an 8" Running Bond, Two-Wythe Intersecting Brick Wall

Name_____

Date_____

Instructor _____

Period _____

Objective

After completing this job you will be able to lay an 8" running bond, two-wythe intersecting brick wall using proper technique.

Equipment

To complete this job you will need the following tools and materials:

- ❖ Mason's tools
- ❖ Mortar
- ❖ Supply of bricks
- ❖ Metal Z-shaped ties

Recommended Procedure

Study the appropriate section in Chapter 10 (Laying Brick) before starting this job.

Intersecting brick walls are often necessary in the construction of most brick structures. They are laid out so that the courses are tied together to form an integrated unit. The individual units are placed so that they interlock the wall segments together. Reinforcement ties (Z-shaped ties) are generally used.

1. Study Illustration 22-1 to see the first course configuration. Locate the face of the walls on the floor and snap a chalk line to preserve the location.

Completed ☐

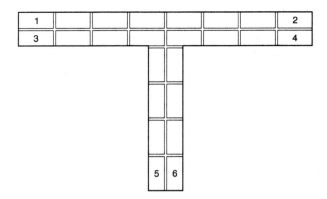

Illustration 22-1. First course.

2. Lay out the first course using no mortar (dry bond) to maintain proper spacing and identify any difficulties or problems. See Illustration 22-1.

Completed ❑

3. Spread the mortar bed and lay the face wythe beginning with brick #1 through brick #2. Level, align, and plumb the course of bricks.

Completed ❑

4. Lay the backing wythe beginning with brick #3 and continuing to brick #4. Do not forget to butter the back side of each brick where the backing wythe sits against the face course. This joint (collar joint) should be completely filled. Level, align, and plumb the course and check the wall thickness.

Completed ❑

5. Lay the intersecting wall brick beginning with brick #5 and then brick #6, running each course to the outside wall. Level, align, and plumb each course and check the wall thickness. This will complete the first course plan.

Completed ❑

6. Lay the second course following the layout shown in Illustration 22-2. Level, align, and plumb the course. Notice how the intersecting wall is interlocked with the outside wall.

Completed ❑

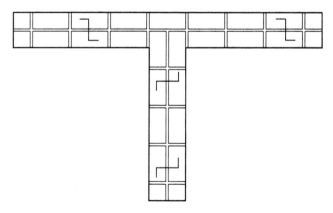

Illustration 22-2. Second course.

Name_____

7. Locate the metal Z-shaped ties as shown in the second course layout plan. Embed the metal ties in a mortar bed and lay the third course identical to the first. Metal ties will be added again on the eighth course in the wall.

Completed ❏

8. Continue laying courses alternating the pattern used in the first and second courses until the wall has reached eight courses high. Refer to Illustration 22-3.

Completed ❏

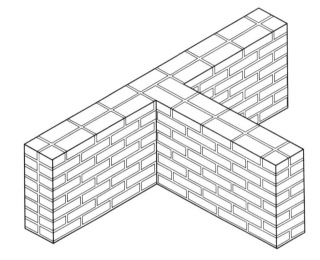

Illustration 22-3. Pictorial view.

9. Level and plumb the completed wall and clean off any mortar splatter.

Completed ❏

10. Tool the joints with a concave jointer when the mortar is thumbprint hard. Tool the head joints first, then the bed joints. Use the sled jointer for the bed joints.

Completed ❏

11. Remove any mortar tailings that remain after finishing the joints. Clean the wall by brushing with a bricklayer's brush.

Completed ❏

12. Clean up the area and return any unused materials and tools to their proper places.

Completed ❏

Instructor's Initials:_____

Date: _____

Job Practice 22 Review ▰▰▰▰

After completing this job successfully, answer the following questions correctly:

1. What kind of metal ties are generally used to tie the two wythes together in an 8″ running bond, two-wythe wall? _____

   _____

2. In addition to the metal ties, how are the wythes bonded together? _____

   _____

3. How is the intersecting wall bonded to the outside wall? _____

   _____

   _____

4. Which joints, head joints or bed joints, are tooled first? _____

   _____

5. What is the operation that follows removing the fins or tailings? _____

   _____

   _____

Score: _____

Job Practice 23
Laying a 12" Common Bond, Solid Brick Wall with Leads

Brick Masonry

Name_____

Date_____

Instructor_____

Period_____

Objective

After completing this job you will be able to lay a 12" common bond, solid brick wall with leads using proper technique.

Equipment

To complete this job you will need the following tools and materials:

❖ Mason's tools

❖ Mortar

❖ Supply of bricks

Recommended Procedure

Study the appropriate section in Chapter 10 (Laying Brick) before starting this job.

The 12" solid wall is essentially an 8" solid wall with a third wythe added. Illustration 23-1 shows the first course which is repeated every sixth or seventh course. It contains three-quarter closures, quarter closures, stretchers, and headers arranged in a specific configuration. Headers are visible on the outer face of the wall.

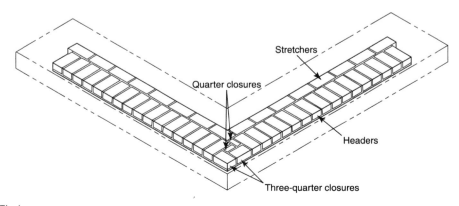

Illustration 23-1. First course.

1. Lay out the wall location such that the inside wall line is equal to the length of one brick plus a mortar joint plus the width of a brick. (This is approximately 12".) Your instructor will specify the length of the wall and lead tails.   Completed ☐

2. Lay the first corner following the design shown in Illustration 23-1.   Completed ☐

3. Study the second course layout shown in Illustration 23-2. Then lay this course on the first corner lead. The second course is composed of stretchers, headers, and quarter closures. The stretchers are visible on the outer face and headers show on the inside. The quarter closures are generally placed after the headers and stretchers are laid.   Completed ☐

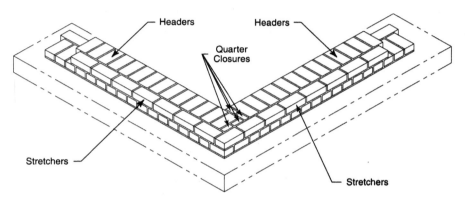

Illustration 23-2. Second course.

4. Lay the third course of the first corner lead as shown in Illustration 23-3. The third course is composed of all stretchers. This pattern is continued for the fourth and fifth courses in typical running bond. Lay these courses.   Completed ☐

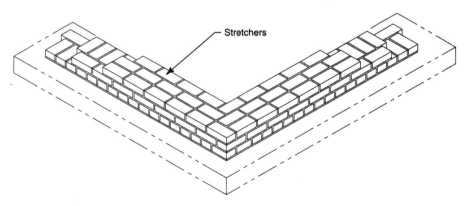

Illustration 23-3. Third course.

5. Lay the sixth course identical to the first course. Tool the joints and brush the bricks.   Completed ☐

Name_____

6. Lay the other lead corner following the procedure above to a height of six courses. Tool the joints and brush these bricks.   Completed ❑

7. Complete the wall by laying each course in the pattern already begun in the leads. Work from both leads toward the center.   Completed ❑

8. Inspect your work, clean up the area, and return the unused materials and tools to their assigned places.   Completed ❑

Twelve-inch brick masonry walls are rare today, but may be used as thermal storage units. Solid, dark colored bricks should be used for this application as solid bricks provide more mass than hollow or cored bricks and dark bricks absorb heat more efficiently than lighter colored units.

Instructor's Initials:_____

Date: _____

Job Practice 23 Review ■■■■■■■■■■■■■■■■■■■■■■■■■■■

After completing this job successfully, answer the following questions correctly:

1. The 12″ solid brick wall is very similar to what other type brick wall? _____

_____

2. The first course of a 12″ solid brick wall is composed of headers and stretchers. On which face are the headers visible? _____

_____

_____

3. How often is the first course configuration repeated in a 12″ solid brick wall? _____

_____

_____

4. What three types of bricks are used in the second course of a 12″ solid brick wall? _____

_____

_____

5. Describe the brick pattern used in the third, fourth, and fifth courses of a 12″ solid brick wall. _____

_____

_____

Score: _____

Job Practice **24**

Building a Corner in Flemish Bond with Quarter Closures

Name_____

Date_____

Instructor _____

Period _____

Objective

After completing this job you will be able to build a corner in Flemish bond with quarter closures using proper technique.

Equipment

To complete this job you will need the following tools and materials:

❖ Mason's tools

❖ Mortar

❖ Supply of bricks

Recommended Procedure

Study the appropriate section in Chapter 10 (Laying Brick) before starting this job. Laying up a corner is very similar for most bonds. After a beginner has built several of the more common ones, they should have little difficulty raising any corner.

1. The Flemish bond is very popular. It is easy to lay, producing an artistic and pleasing wall. It is more costly than the common bond and requires greater care, but is worth the effort. See Illustration 24-1 for the pattern.

Completed ❏

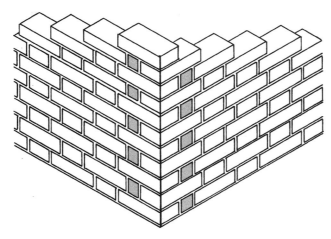

Illustration 24-1. Flemish bond corner with quarter closure.

2. The bond consists of alternate headers and stretchers in each course. The headers are centered on the stretchers between each course. The bond is started at the corner with a stretcher and then a quarter closure along the opposite tail. Lay the first course of brick.

Completed ☐

3. Lay the remaining courses following the pattern shown in Illustration 24-1. Your instructor will specify the height of the corner.

Completed ☐

4. Tool the joints and brush the bricks.

Completed ☐

5. Inspect your work, clean up the area, and return unused materials and tools to their assigned places.

Completed ☐

Instructor's Initials:_____

Date: _____

Job Practice 24 Review

After completing this job successfully, answer the following questions correctly:

1. How does the Flemish bond with quarter closures get its name? _____

_____

_____

2. Why is the Flemish bond with quarter closures more costly?

_____

_____

Name_____

3. If this type of wall takes more time and materials, then why build it? _____

_____

4. Which courses have headers? _____

_____

5. When should one brush the wall? _____

_____

_____

_____

Score: _____

Job Practice 25
Building a Corner in Flemish Bond with Three-Quarter Closures

Name_____

Date_____

Instructor_____

Period _____

Objective

After completing this job you will be able to build a corner in Flemish bond with three-quarter closures using proper technique.

Equipment

To complete this job you will need the following tools and materials:

- ❖ Mason's tools
- ❖ Mortar
- ❖ Supply of bricks

Recommended Procedure

Study the appropriate section in Chapter 10 (Laying Brick) before starting this job. Laying up a corner or wall in Flemish bond using three-quarter closures is identical to building a wall using quarter closures (Job Practice 24) except that three-quarter closures are used instead of quarter closures.

1. The Flemish bond using three-quarter closures is a popular bond. Refer to Illustration 25-1 to see the pattern. Study the drawing before beginning work.

Completed ☐

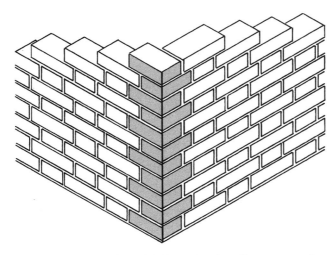

Illustration 25-1. Flemish bond using three-quarter closures at corner.

2. The bond consists of alternate headers and stretchers in each course. The headers are centered on the stretchers between each course. The bond is started at the corner with a three-quarter closure and then a stretcher along the opposite tail. Lay the first course of bricks.   Completed ☐

3. Lay the remaining courses following the pattern shown in Illustration 25-1. Your instructor will specify the height of the corner.   Completed ☐

4. Tool the joints and brush the bricks.   Completed ☐

5. Inspect your work, clean up the area, and return unused materials and tools to their assigned places.   Completed ☐

Instructor's Initials:_____

Date: _____

Job Practice 25 Review

After completing this job successfully, answer the following questions correctly:

1. How is the Flemish bond with three-quarter closures different from the Flemish bond with quarter closures? _____

_____

_____

2. Describe the brick pattern in a corner laid in Flemish bond with three-quarter closures. _____

_____

_____

_____

Name_____

3. What are the disadvantages of using the Flemish bond with three-quarter closures? _____

_____

_____

4. What are the advantages of a Flemish bond wall with three-quarter closures? _____

_____

_____

5. What are the pieces of brick left over from cutting the three-quarter closures called? _____

_____

Score: _____

Job Practice **26**
Building a Corner in English Bond with Quarter Closures

Brick Masonry

Name_____

Date_____

Instructor _____

Period _____

Objective

After completing this job you will be able to build a corner in English bond with quarter closures using proper technique.

Equipment

To complete this job you will need the following tools and materials:

- ❖ Mason's tools
- ❖ Mortar
- ❖ Supply of bricks

Recommended Procedure

Study the appropriate section in Chapter 10 (Laying Brick) before starting this job.

1. The English bond has alternate courses of stretchers and headers. The headers center on the stretchers and on the joints between the stretchers. The stretchers all line up vertically, one over the other. See Illustration 26-1 for the pattern.

Completed ☐

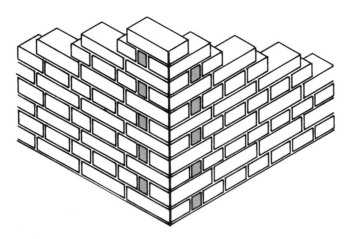

Illustration 26-1. English bond with quarter closures.

2. The bond is started at the corner with a stretcher along one tail and a quarter closure along the other tail. Notice that stretchers are continued along one side while headers are used along the other side. Lay the first course.

Completed ☐

3. Reverse the pattern for the second course. Lay the second course.

Completed ☐

4. Continue laying up the wall alternating courses as shown in Illustration 26-1 until the desired height is reached.

Completed ☐

5. Tool the joints and brush the bricks.

Completed ☐

6. Inspect your work, clean up the area, and return unused materials and tools to their assigned places.

Completed ☐

Instructor's Initials:_____

Date: _____

Job Practice 26 Review

After completing this job successfully, answer the following questions correctly:

1. What is the most dominant pattern in an English bond with quarter closures?_____

_____

_____

Name_____

2. How are the headers positioned with respect to the stretchers in an English bond with quarter closures? _____

_____

_____

3. What is the pattern of the stretcher in an English bond with quarter closures? _____

_____

_____

4. Is this bond very practical for a single wythe wall? Why? _____

_____

_____

5. Is it possible to build an English bond wall without using any quarter closures?_____

_____

_____

Score: _____

Job Practice 27
Building a Corner in English Bond with Three-Quarter Closures

Brick Masonry

Name_____

Date_____

Instructor _____

Period _____

Objective

After completing this job you will be able to build a corner in English bond with three-quarter closures using proper technique.

Equipment

To complete this job you will need the following tools and materials:

❖ Mason's tools

❖ Mortar

❖ Supply of bricks

Recommended Procedure

Study the appropriate section in Chapter 10 (Laying Brick) before starting this job.

1. The English bond has alternate courses of stretchers and headers. The headers center on the stretchers and on the joints between the stretchers. The stretchers all line up vertically, one over the other. See Illustration 27-1 for the pattern.

Completed ☐

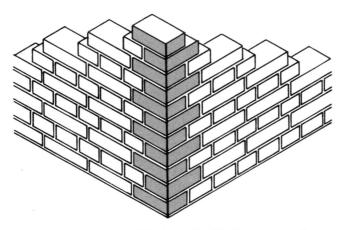

Illustration 27-1. English bond with three-quarter closures.

2. The bond is started at the corner with a three-quarter closure along one tail and a header along the other tail. Notice that stretchers are continued along one side while headers are used along the other side. Lay the first course.   Completed ☐

3. Reverse the pattern for the second course. Lay the second course.   Completed ☐

4. Continue laying up the wall alternating courses as shown in Illustration 27-1 until the desired height is reached.   Completed ☐

5. Tool the joints and brush the bricks.   Completed ☐

6. Inspect your work, clean up the area, and return unused materials and tools to their assigned places.   Completed ☐

Instructor's Initials:_____

Date: _____

Job Practice 27 Review

After completing this job successfully, answer the following questions correctly:

1. How does a corner in English bond with three-quarter closures differ from one using quarter closures? _____

_____

_____

_____

Name_____

2. Is the English bond very practical for a single wythe wall? Why? _____

   _____

   _____

3. In a four course corner in English bond with three-quarter closures, how many of the courses will have headers? _____

   _____

4. How does the appearance of an English bond wall with three-quarter closures compare with an English bond wall with quarter closures (not the corners)? _____

   _____

5. Would the English bond be more practical if the wall were an 8″ solid brick wall? Why? _____

   _____

   _____

Score: _____

Job Practice 28

Constructing a 10″ Brick Masonry Cavity Wall with Metal Ties and Weep Holes

Brick Masonry

Name_____

Date_____

Instructor _____

Period _____

Objective

After completing this job you will be able to construct a 10″ brick masonry cavity wall with metal ties and weep holes using proper technique.

Equipment

To complete this job you will need the following tools and materials:

- ❖ Mason's tools
- ❖ Mortar
- ❖ Supply of bricks
- ❖ Metal ties (Z type)
- ❖ Four 6″ oiled rods or wick
- ❖ One drop stick 1 3/4″ × 3/4″ × 48″ long
- ❖ Eye protection for cutting bricks

Recommended Procedure

Study the appropriate section in Chapter 10 (Laying Brick) before starting this job. No changes are required in basic bricklaying techniques in the construction of a cavity wall. One principle, however, is that no bridge of solid material capable of carrying water across the minimum 2″ cavity space shall be permitted. The construction of two separate wythes, with a clean cavity, is the objective.

1. Study Illustration 28-1 before starting work on the cavity wall.　　　　　　　Completed ☐

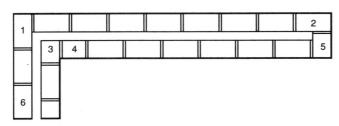

Illustration 28-1. First course.

2. Snap chalk lines to establish the wall location. Determine the length of both sections of the wall by counting the bricks in Illustration 28-1.

                        Completed ❑

3. Set up the work area with two mortar boards, one on either side of the wall. Stack bricks on either side of both mortar boards.

                        Completed ❑

4. Lay out the first course dry as shown in the first course plan and mark the position of each brick.

                        Completed ❑

5. Lay the inside bed course beginning with brick #1 and continuing to brick #2 in a full mortar bed. Work from both ends to the middle. Level and plumb these bricks. The bricks should be laid to #6 on the modular rule. Lay brick #6 and fill in the course between #1 and #6.

                        Completed ❑

6. Lay brick #5 and the one adjacent to it. Lay bricks #3 and #4 to the line. Be sure all corners are square. Fill in the bricks to complete the first course. Check your work to be sure it is level, plumb, and straight.

                        Completed ❑

7. If you did not use empty head joints for the four weep holes shown in the elevation plan, Illustration 28-2, open those joints or use any one of the methods of forming a weep hole—oiled rod, rope wick, or metal or plastic tubing. Be sure the two tiers of masonry are the same height and level.

                        Completed ❑

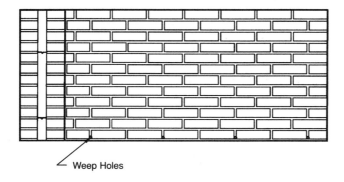

Weep Holes

Illustration 28-2. Elevation.

Name_____

8. Cut 3 three-quarter brick for the second course and lay the mortar bed for the second course. Bevel the mortar bed to avoid dropping mortar into the cavity. Lay the second course of brick as shown in Illustration 28-3. Lay three-quarter brick #7 at the right end of the wall over bed bricks #2 and #5. Note the cross joints are centered on the bricks below. Keep the cavity clean. Lay the second course brick #8 at the other end of the wall and complete the wythe between them. Complete the second course.

Completed ❑

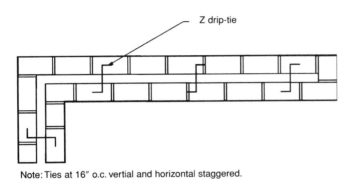

Note: Ties at 16″ o.c. vertial and horizontal staggered.

Illustration 28-3. Second course.

9. Install the Z ties in the position shown on the second course plan. They should be set in a mortar bed with the drip pointing down.

Completed ❑

10. Lay the third course, being careful not to drop any mortar into the cavity. Install the drop stick on the metal ties moving it along to prevent mortar from entering the cavity.

Completed ❑

11. Lay the fourth through the eighth courses making sure they are level and straight. Remove the drop stick and insert the Z ties on top of the eighth course as shown in the second course plan.

Completed ❑

12. Install the drop stick on the metal ties and lay the next four courses to complete the wall. Be sure all courses are laid to the #6 on the modular rule.

Completed ❑

13. Strike the mortar joints when the mortar is hard enough. Use the sled runner on the bed joints and the convex tool on the head joints. Brush the wall.

Completed ❑

14. Check to see that the weep holes are clear.

Completed ❑

15. Inspect your work, clean up the area, and return all unused materials and tools to their assigned places.

Completed ❑

Instructor's Initials:_____

Date: _____

Job Practice 28 Review

After completing this job successfully, answer the following questions correctly:

1. Why must the cavity be kept clean of mortar droppings in a cavity wall? _____

   _____

   _____

   _____

2. At what point does an *airspace* become a *cavity*? _____

   _____

3. Why are two mortar boards generally recommended for cavity wall construction? _____

   _____

   _____

4. What is the purpose of a weep hole? _____

   _____

   _____

5. Describe the basic types of weep holes. _____

   _____

   _____

6. What is the function of Z ties in a 10″ brick cavity wall? _____

   _____

   _____

Score: _____

Job Practice 29

Constructing a Reinforced Single Wythe Brick Bearing Wall

Brick Masonry

Name_____

Date_____

Instructor _____

Period _____

Objective

After completing this job you will be able to construct a reinforced single wythe brick bearing wall and install steel reinforcing using proper technique.

Equipment

To complete this job you will need the following tools and materials:

❖ Mason's tools

❖ Mortar

❖ Supply of bricks

❖ Joint reinforcement

❖ 2′ piece of #4 rebar

Recommended Procedure

Study the appropriate section in Chapter 10 (Laying Brick) before starting this job. Brick masonry bearing wall systems have been used for years for their strength and durability. In a single wythe brick bearing wall system, the brick masonry serves as both the structural system and exterior facing. Study Illustration 29-1. This is a 6″ reinforced wall made from 6″ × 4″ × 12″ face brick. The wall has vertical reinforcing of #4 rebar at 48″ o.c. and horizontal 3/16″ diameter reinforcing at 24″ o.c. This is the wall you are to build.

Illustration 29-1. A single wythe brick bearing wall.

1. Set up your work area and snap a line on the floor to maintain the location of the wall. The length of the wall should be about 48″ long. Ask your instructor if this length is satisfactory.   Completed ❑

2. Lay down a full mortar bed to receive the bed course. Be sure not to cover the chalk line with mortar. All joints must be full to resist moisture penetration.   Completed ❑

3. Lay the bed course in running bond keeping the head joints even in thickness and completely filled. Level, plumb, and straightedge the course. Check spacing with your plumb rule.   Completed ❑

4. Lay the second course so that mortar joints are centered on the bricks in the first course. It is very important that the cell holes line up to receive reinforcing and mortar (or grout).   Completed ❑

5. Lay the third course using the same spacing as the first course. Level, plumb, and straightedge the wall. Tool the mortar joints when the mortar is thumbprint hard.   Completed ❑

6. Select a joint reinforcement which is compatible with the brick masonry units being used. Position the joint reinforcement on the top of the third course and embed it in mortar.   Completed ❑

7. Lay the fourth course of bricks similar to the second course spacing. Be sure the reinforcing is completely embedded in mortar and remains in the proper position.   Completed ❑

Name_____

8. Lay the fifth course of bricks similar to the first and third courses. Insert the vertical reinforcing bar (maximum size #6) in a cell near the center of the wall.   Completed ❑

9. Fill the cells containing the vertical reinforcing with mortar. The mortar should be fluid enough to fill the voids, but it should not separate into its constituent parts.   Completed ❑

10. Strike the joints and brush the wall.   Completed ❑

11. Inspect your work, clean up the area, and return unused materials and tools to their proper places.   Completed ❑

Instructor's Initials:_____

Date: _____

Job Practice 29 Review ▰▰▰▰▰▰▰▰▰▰▰▰▰▰

After completing this job successfully, answer the following questions correctly:

1. What is the difference between a wythe and a course of bricks? _____
_____
_____
_____

2. What are the two functions served in a single wythe brick bearing wall system? _____
_____
_____

3. Is it always necessary to have both horizontal as well as vertical reinforcing in a single wythe brick bearing wall? Why? _____
_____
_____

4. Why was it necessary for the cell holes to line up in the wall you built? _____
_____
_____

5. What is the maximum recommended size of vertical reinforcing to be used in a reinforced single wythe brick bearing wall? _____
_____

Score: _____

Job Practice **30**
Corbelling a 12″ Brick Wall

Name_____

Date_____

Instructor _____

Period _____

Objective

After completing this job you will be able to corbel a brick wall using proper technique.

Equipment

To complete this job you will need the following tools and materials:

- ❖ Mason's tools
- ❖ Mortar
- ❖ Supply of bricks

Recommended Procedure

Study the appropriate section in Chapter 10 (Laying Brick) before starting this job.

Corbelling is a method used by masons to widen a wall by projecting out masonry units to form a ledge or shelf. When building a corbel, each brick course extends out further than the one below it. As a general rule, a masonry unit should not extend out further than one-third the width or one-half the height, whichever is less.

In view of the fact that corbels normally support a load, they must be carefully constructed. Headers are generally used to tie the corbel into the base. Building codes generally require the top course to be a full header course. All joints must be completely filled with mortar.

1. Study Illustration 30-1. Snap a line on the foundation or base where the front edge of the wall is to be constructed.

Completed ❑

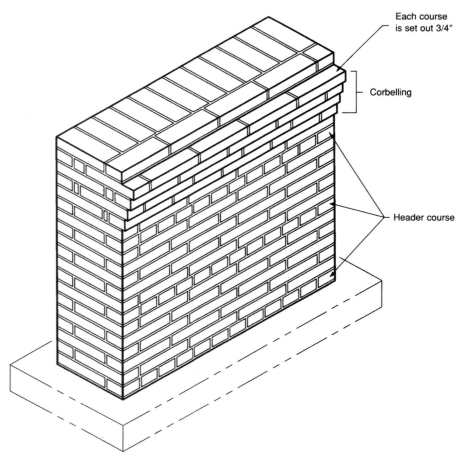

Each course
is set out 3/4"

Corbelling

Header course

Illustration 30-1. Corbelling a brick wall.

2. Lay out the first course as a dry course to check the spacing. Running bond will be used with a header course every seventh course.

Completed ❏

3. Lay the first course with headers on the front wythe and stretchers on the back. Use a full mortar bed. Level, plumb, and square the bricks. Check the spacing.

Completed ❏

4. Lay the second through sixth courses. Check the height of each course as it is laid and be sure bed joints are uniform and level.

Completed ❏

5. Lay the seventh course as a header course with full mortar joints.

Completed ❏

6. Continue to lay the wall until you reach the height where the corbel course is to begin. Check your progress often to be sure it is plumb and straight.

Completed ❏

7. Begin the corbel course by projecting headers out 3/4" beyond the course below. Fill the extra wide head joint with mortar.

Completed ❏

8. Lay the second corbel course using stretchers along the front and headers along the back wythe. Fill in the space between with bats. Be sure the course is level and straight.

Completed ❏

Name_____

9. Lay the third corbel course using stretchers on the front and back wythes and three-quarter headers between the wythes. Each corbel should project out 3/4" beyond the course below.   Completed ☐

10. Lay the next course the same as the first course of the wall—headers on the front wythe and stretchers on the back wythe. Continue the wall to the desired height.   Completed ☐

11. Finish all joints when the mortar is hard enough to tool.   Completed ☐

12. Clean the wall with the trowel and brush.   Completed ☐

13. Inspect your work, clean up the area, and return unused materials and tools to their assigned places.   Completed ☐

Instructor's Initials:_____

Date: _____

Job Practice 30 Review ▬▬▬▬▬▬▬▬▬▬▬▬▬▬▬▬▬▬▬▬▬▬

After completing this job successfully, answer the following questions correctly:

1. What is the function of a corbel in a masonry wall?_____

   _____

2. When corbelling, what is the maximum distance that a brick can be extended out beyond the unit below it? _____

   _____

   _____

   _____

3. What bonding technique is generally used to tie the corbel to the base? _____

   _____

4. What is the maximum angle of a corbel measured from the horizontal?_____

   _____

5. What is important to remember about mortar joints in corbels?_____

   _____

   _____

Score: _____

Job Practice 31
Building a Hollow Brick Masonry Pier

Brick Masonry

Name_____

Date_____

Instructor _____

Period _____

Objective

After completing this job you will be able to build a 16" × 20" hollow brick masonry pier using proper technique.

Equipment

To complete this job you will need the following tools and materials:

❖ Mason's tools

❖ Mortar

❖ Supply of bricks

Recommended Procedure

Study the appropriate section in Chapter 10 (Laying Brick) before starting this job.

Piers are similar to columns except they are shorter and generally do not support a load. They are commonly used as gateposts at corners or openings or ends of a wall. Piers can be constructed using a one-wythe wall 4" thick. The bond pattern is usually staggered so that the wall is tied together from a different side in each course in an interlocking fashion. Weep holes may be required. Study Illustration 31-1.

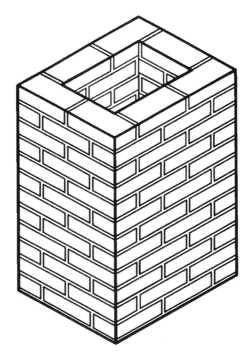

Illustration 31-1. Pictorial view.

1. Study Illustration 31-2 to see the pattern used in the first course. Snap a line to preserve the location of the pier.

Completed ❑

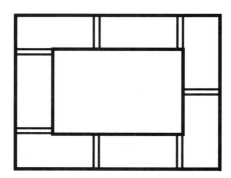

Illustration 31-2. First course.

2. Lay the bed course on a generous mortar bed. Check the bricks to be sure they are level and straight and that the corners are square. You may use either 1/2″ or 3/8″ joints depending on the type of bricks used. Refer to the first course plan above.

Completed ❑

3. Lay the second course as shown in the second course plan. See Illustration 31-3. Bricks should be positioned so that head joints are offset to provide an interlocking connection. Level, plumb, and square the course.

Completed ❑

Name_____

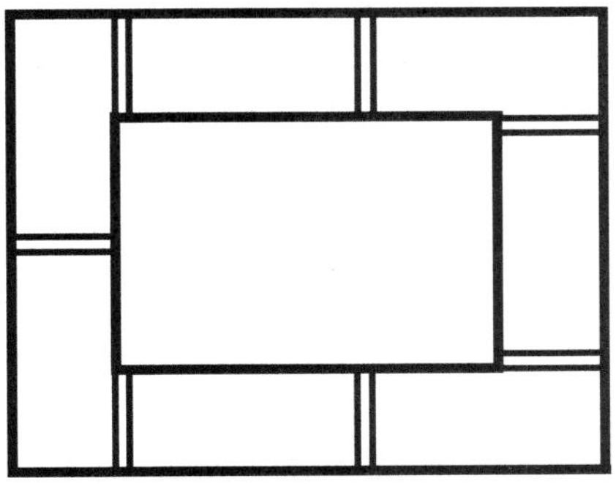

Illustration 31-3. Second course.

4. Lay successive courses alternating the patterns used in the first and second courses until the pier has reached the desired height. Twelve courses should be adequate for practice. Avoid dropping any mortar inside the pier.   Completed ❏

5. When the mortar is thumbprint hard, tool the joints and clean off any fins with the trowel. Clean the surface with the brush.   Completed ❏

6. Inspect your work, clean up the area, and return any unused materials and tools to their assigned places.   Completed ❏

Instructor's Initials:_____

Date: _____

Job Practice 31 Review ▬▬▬▬▬▬▬▬▬▬▬▬▬▬▬▬

After completing this job successfully, answer the following questions correctly:

1. What is the difference between a pier and a column? _____

_____

_____

2. How did the pier that you constructed gain its strength since no reinforcing was used?_____

_____

_____

3. If weep holes had been required in your pier, where should they have been located? _____

_____

_____

4. How did you know it was time to tool (strike) the joints? _____

_____

_____

5. What tool did you use to check the first course of masonry to be sure the pier was square? _____

_____

6. How are fins generally removed from brick masonry? _____

_____

Score: _____

Job Practice 32
Cleaning New Brick Masonry with Acid Solutions

Brick Masonry

Name_____

Date_____

Instructor_____

Period _____

Objective

After completing this job you will be able to clean new brick masonry with acid solutions using proper technique.

Equipment

To complete this job you will need the following tools and materials:

- ❖ Safety protection for eyes and skin
- ❖ Long-handled stiff fiber brush
- ❖ Mixing bucket (plastic)
- ❖ Wood paddle or scraper
- ❖ Trisodium phosphate
- ❖ Household detergent
- ❖ Hydrochloric (muriatic) acid
- ❖ Potassium or sodium hydroxide

Recommended Procedure

Study the appropriate section in Chapter 10 (Laying Brick) before starting this job.

The finished appearance of a masonry wall depends not only on the skill used in laying the units, but on the cleaning procedure as well. The appearance of a masonry structure may be ruined by improper cleaning. All cleaning should be applied to a sample test area of approximately 20 sq. ft. It will usually take a minimum of one week to see the results of cleaning.

1. A solution of hydrochloric acid is used extensively as a cleaning agent for new masonry, but the first procedure requires no acid. When the masonry is thoroughly set and cured, begin the cleaning operation.

Completed ☐

2. Remove large particles of mortar with wood paddles or scrapers before wetting the wall. A chisel or wire brush might be necessary.   Completed ☐

3. Saturate the wall with clean water and flush away all loose mortar and dirt.   Completed ☐

4. Scrub down the wall with a solution of 1/2 cup of trisodium phosphate and 1/2 cup of household detergent dissolved in one gallon of clean water. Use a stiff fiber brush.   Completed ☐

5. Rinse off all cleaning solution and mortar particles using clean water under pressure.   Completed ☐

6. When acid cleaning becomes necessary on dark colored bricks, follow steps 1 through 3 above and then use a clean, stain-free commercial grade hydrochloric (muriatic) acid—mix one part of acid to nine parts water. Mix in a nonmetallic container.

⚠ **Warning!** Pour the acid into the water, not the water into the acid! Be careful with this chemical and wear eye and skin protection.

Use a long-handled fiber brush to scrub the wall.   Completed ☐

7. Keep the area not being cleaned flushed free of acid and dissolved mortar. This scum, if allowed to dry, may be impossible to remove later.   Completed ☐

8. Scrub the bricks, not the mortar joints. Do not use metal tools. Clean only a small area at a time.   Completed ☐

9. Rinse the wall thoroughly with plenty of clean water while it is still wet from scrubbing with the acid.   Completed ☐

10. When cleaning light colored brick, use the highest grade acid available. It should be free of any yellow or brown coloration. Mix 1 part acid with 15 parts water. After scrubbing, neutralize with a solution of potassium or sodium hydroxide, consisting of 1/2 lb. hydroxide to 1 qt. of water (2 lb. per gal.). Allow this to remain on the wall for two or three days before washing again with clean water.   Completed ☐

Instructor's Initials:_____

Date: _____

Name_____

Job Practice 32 Review ━━━━━━━━━━━━━━━

After completing this job successfully, answer the following questions correctly:

1. How long should you usually wait to see the effect of using a cleaning solution on a brick wall?____
   _____

2. What is the most popular acid used to clean brick walls? _____
   _____

3. What personal safety precautions should be taken when cleaning a brick wall with acid? _____
   _____
   _____

4. What is the usual mixing proportions of muriatic acid to water? _____
   _____
   _____

5. What precautions should be taken when mixing acid and water together?_____
   _____
   _____
   _____

6. What should you do before scrubbing a brick wall with acid? _____
   _____
   _____
   _____

7. Why shouldn't you scrub the mortar joints with acid? _____
   _____
   _____

Score:_____

Job Practice **33**
Handling Concrete Blocks

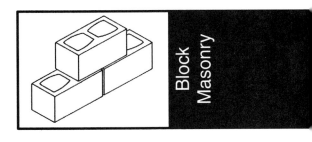

Name _____

Date _____

Instructor _____

Period _____

Objective

After completing this job you will be able to handle concrete blocks using proper technique.

Equipment

To complete this job you will need the following tools and materials:

- ❖ Mason's tools
- ❖ Mortar
- ❖ Several 8″ × 8″ × 16″ concrete blocks

Recommended Procedure

Study the appropriate section in Chapter 11 (Laying Block) before starting this job. Concrete blocks are large units that generally require both hands for placement. For example, a typical 8″ × 8″ × 16″ concrete block made with sand and gravel aggregates weighs between 22 lb. and 28 lb. depending on the specific aggregate used. Review Job Practice 10.

1. Form a mortar bed for concrete block. Place one block (no head joint) on the mortar bed. Use both hands to lift the block, Illustration 33-1. Grasp the web at each end of the block to lay it on the mortar bed. Even movements are preferred to jerking motions.

Completed ☐

Illustration 33-1. Placing a concrete block on the mortar bed.

2. The trowel should remain in your hand while placing the block to save time when only one or two blocks are set. If several blocks have been prepared, then the trowel may be laid aside while the blocks are placed on the mortar bed. Lift the block slowly and move to the location where it is to be placed.

Completed ☐

3. By tipping the block slightly forward toward you when you place it on the mortar bed and looking down the face of the block, you can position the block in proper position with respect to the top edge of the course below. See Illustration 33-2.

Completed ☐

Illustration 33-2. Placing a block in the wall.

Name_____

4. Then roll the block back slightly to correctly align the top of the block with the line. During this movement, the block should be pressed toward the last block to form a good head joint. Mortar should squeeze out slightly.   Completed ❑

5. Blocks are positioned in a wall with the wide flange on the top. This provides a wider space for the bed joint. As each block is laid, the excess mortar should be cut off with the trowel held at a slight angle to the block.   Completed ❑

6. Practice setting several blocks on the mortar bed using the procedure described above.   Completed ❑

7. Clean up the work area, remove mortar from the floor and blocks, and return all materials and tools to their assigned places.   Completed ❑

Instructor's Initials:_____

Date: _____

Job Practice 33 Review ▬▬▬▬▬▬▬▬▬▬▬▬▬▬▬▬▬

After completing this job successfully, answer the following questions correctly:

1. What is the approximate weight of a typical concrete block ($8'' \times 8'' \times 16''$)? _____

_____

2. Describe the recommended method of grasping a concrete block._____

_____

_____

_____

3. Why are smooth, even movements recommended when placing a concrete block on the mortar bed? _____

_____

4. Why is the concrete block tipped forward when placing it in the wall?_____

_____

_____

_____

5. Is the wide flange of the block placed facing up or down? Why?_____

_____

_____

_____

Score: _____

Job Practice 34
Laying an 8" Running Bond Concrete Block Wall

Name_____

Date_____

Instructor _____

Period _____

Objective

After completing this job you will be able to lay an 8" running bond concrete block wall using proper technique.

Equipment

To complete this job you will need the following tools and materials:

❖ Mason's tools

❖ Mortar

❖ Supply of blocks

Recommended Procedure

Study the appropriate section of Chapter 11 (Laying Blocks) before starting this job.

A well planned concrete block structure will involve mainly stretcher and corner blocks. See Illustration 34-1 These blocks are nominally 8" × 8" × 16". Actual size is 7 5/8" × 7 5/8" × 15 5/8". This allows for a 3/8" mortar joint that is standard.

Concrete blocks must be protected from excess moisture before use. If they are wet when placed, they will shrink when dry and cause cracks. Protect them from rain.

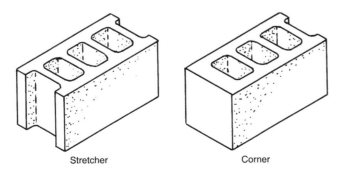

Stretcher   Corner

Illustration 34-1. These are the two primary concrete blocks used.

1. Collect materials and tools needed and set up a work area. Establish the outside wall line with a chalk line. This line should be checked for squareness and proper length before proceeding to the next step. Ask your instructor which length of wall to build. This job procedure follows the photographic sequence in the text (Chapter 11).   Completed ❑

2. String out the block for the first course without mortar to check the layout. Allow 3/8″ for each mortar joint. Set the blocks aside when you are satisfied with the layout.   Completed ❑

3. Spread a full mortar bed and furrow it with the trowel. Provide plenty of mortar on which to set the blocks.   Completed ❑

4. Lay the corner block, positioning it carefully and accurately. Concrete blocks should be laid with the thicker edge of the face shell up to provide a wider mortar bed.   Completed ❑

5. Lay several stretcher blocks along the wall line. Several blocks can be buttered on the end of the face shells if they are stood on end. This speeds the operation. To place them, push them downward into the mortar bed and sideways against the previously laid block.   Completed ❑

6. After three or four blocks have been placed into position, they may be aligned, leveled, and plumbed with the mason's level. Tap on the block rather than the level.   Completed ❑

7. After the first course has been laid, the corner lead is built up as in Illustration 34-2. This corner is very important since the remainder of the wall is dependent upon its accuracy. The lead corner is usually laid up to four or five courses high above the center of the wall. Each course is checked to be sure it is aligned, level, and plumb as it is laid.   Completed ❑

Illustration 34-2. A typical concrete block lead.

Name_____

8. Construct the other lead so that a mason's line can be used to indicate the proper height of each course between the corners. Use line blocks, line pins, or adjustable line holders. Work from the corners toward the center of the wall. Do not allow a block to touch the line.   Completed ❏

9. Complete the wall by laying to the line. Keep each block a line width away from the line and even at the bottom of the course.   Completed ❏

10. Tool the mortar joints with the concave or V-joint tool. The tool should be slightly larger than the width of the mortar joint. A 5/8″ diameter bar is usually used for a 3/8″ concave mortar joint and a 1/2″ square bar is used for making a 3/8″ V-shaped joint. Tools for tooling horizontal mortar joints should be at least 22″ long. Remove tags with the trowel.   Completed ❏

11. When the mortar is sufficiently dry, the wall may be brushed or rubbed with a stiff fiber brush or a burlap bag to remove dried particles.   Completed ❏

12. Inspect your work, clean up the area, and return tools and materials to their assigned places.   Completed ❏

Instructor's Initials:_____

Date: _____

Job Practice 34 Review

After completing this job successfully, answer the following questions correctly:

1. What two types of blocks are most well-planned concrete block walls composed of? _____
   _____

2. What is the standard mortar joint thickness used with concrete blocks?_____

3. What is the actual size of an 8″ × 8″ × 16″ concrete block? _____

4. Why are concrete blocks not wet before they are laid? _____
   _____
   _____

5. What kind of bed is laid down for the first course of concrete blocks in a wall? _____
   _____

6. Why is the height of each course so critical in a lead? _____
   _____
   _____

7. How high is the lead corner generally in a concrete block wall? _____

Score: _____

Job Practice 35

Laying a 10" Concrete Block Cavity Wall

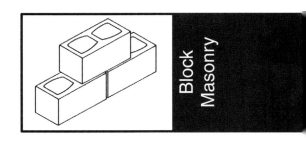

Name_____

Date_____

Instructor_____

Period_____

Objective

After completing this job you will be able to lay a 10" concrete block cavity wall using proper technique.

Equipment

To complete this job you will need the following tools and materials:

- ❖ Mason's tools
- ❖ Mortar
- ❖ Supply of blocks
- ❖ Rectangular metal ties
- ❖ Weep hole wicking
- ❖ Rigid foam insulation (optional)
- ❖ Board to catch mortar droppings

Recommended Procedure

Study the appropriate section of Chapter 11 (Laying Block) before starting this job.

A cavity wall consists of two walls (wythes) separated by a continuous air space 2" to 4 1/2" wide. The wythes are tied securely together with noncorroding metal ties that are embedded in the mortar joints. See Illustration 35-1. Unit ties are generally placed at every other block horizontally and in every other horizontal joint. Continuous metal joint reinforcement could be used instead.

Weep holes and flashing at the bottom of the wall need special attention if the wall is to be water resistant. Weep holes should be located in the bottom course at about every second or third head joint in the outside wythe. The cavity must be kept free of mortar droppings that could form a bridge between the wythes.

Illustration 35-1. Rectangular ties used in cavity wall construction.

1. Set up the work area and stock it with a good supply of 4″ × 8″ × 16″ concrete blocks. Lay down a full bed of mortar for the inside wythe. This bed must be watertight.

Completed ❑

2. Place the blocks for the first course of the inside wythe. Be sure all head joints are solid and watertight.

Completed ❑

3. Position the flashing over the top edge of the first inside course and rest it on the foundation (under the outside wythe). Embed the flashing with mortar between the first and second course of the inside wythe.

Completed ❑

4. Lay the first course of the outside wythe allowing 2″ continuous air space between the wythes. The flashing will be beneath this course. Maintain weep holes between every second or third block. Insert wick or other acceptable material. Keep the cavity clean as the work proceeds up to the second course.

Completed ❑

5. Lay the second outer course with full bed and head joints. Be sure all joints and holes are filled with mortar. Do not allow any mortar to fall into the cavity. Mortar can be spread about 1/2″ back from the edge of the cavity to reduce the chance of falling into the cavity. If rigid insulation is to be used in the wall, now is the time to install it. It should be placed against the inside wythe and should not prevent the escape of moisture from the cavity. A 1″ air space should always be maintained as the minimum.

Completed ❑

Name_____

6. Position rectangular unit ties over the second course of the two wythes. Be sure they are the same height. Embed the ties within the mortar joint under the third course on the inside wythe.   Completed ❑

7. Lay the third outer course with the reinforcement embedded in the mortar joint.   Completed ❑

8. Place a board on the ties to catch mortar droppings as the next course is laid. It will be removed when the next reinforcement is placed.   Completed ❑

9. Repeat the procedure until the wall has reached the desired height.   Completed ❑

0. Inspect your work, clean up the area, and return all tools and materials to their proper places.   Completed ❑

Instructor's Initials:_____

Date: _____

Job Practice 35 Review

After completing this job successfully, answer the following questions correctly:

1. How often are metal ties generally placed in a 10″ concrete block cavity wall? _____
_____

2. What provision for the escape of moisture did you make in your cavity wall?_____
_____

3. How was the flashing positioned in the wall?_____
_____
_____
_____

4. Why are full bed and head joints so important in cavity wall construction?_____
_____

5. If rigid foam insulation is placed inside the cavity, what is the minimum air space? _____
_____

6. What technique is recommended to catch mortar droppings in the cavity? _____
_____
_____
_____

Score: _____

Job Practice **36**
Laying an 8″ Composite Wall with Concrete Block Backup

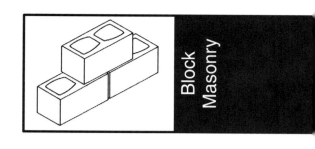

Block Masonry

Name_____

Date_____

Instructor_____

Period _____

Objective

After completing this job you will be able to lay an 8″ composite wall with concrete block backup using proper technique.

Equipment

To complete this job you will need the following tools and materials:

- ❖ Mason's tools
- ❖ Mortar
- ❖ Supply of 4″ × 8″ × 16″ concrete blocks
- ❖ Supply of common bricks
- ❖ Z ties
- ❖ Plasterer's trowel

Recommended Procedure

Study the appropriate section in Chapter 11 (Laying Block) before starting this job.

A composite wall is two wythes bonded together with masonry, metal ties, or joint reinforcement. The two wythes are joined together in a continuous mass using a vertical collar joint that prevents the passage of water through the wall.

Concrete blocks are often used as backup for bricks to make a composite wall. The composite wall that you are to build will be this type of wall. See Illustration 36-1.

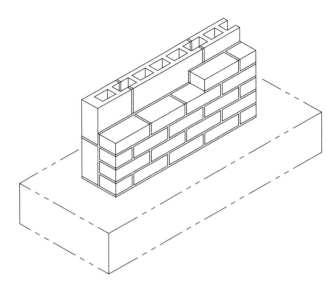

Illustration 36-1. Eight inch composite wall with brick facing and concrete block backup.

1. Arrange your work space and stock it with a good supply of 4″ × 8″ × 16″ concrete blocks and common bricks. Plan to build a wall that is 32″ long and 32″ high.   Completed ☐

2. Snap a chalk line on the floor to preserve the location of the wall. Cut several bricks in half and secure six half blocks or cut your own.   Completed ☐

3. Lay down a mortar bed for the inner wythe of 4″ concrete blocks. Lay a corner block at either end with a half block between them.   Completed ☐

4. Lay the second course of the inner wythe of 4″ concrete blocks. Stagger the mortar joints. Parge the side adjacent to the outer wythe, being careful not to upset the bond. The use of a plasterer's trowel is more efficient than a brick trowel for this operation.   Completed ☐

5. Lay six courses of bricks in running bond to bring the outer wythe to 16″ high. Refer to Illustration 36-1 again. Be sure the vertical collar joint is filled with mortar and the bricks are laid with full bed joints.   Completed ☐

6. Position two Z ties across the wythes about 24″ apart. Embed them in mortar.   Completed ☐

7. Bring the wall up another course of concrete blocks to produce a height of 32″. Complete the outer wythe of bricks.   Completed ☐

Name_____

8. Strike the joints and brush the completed wall.   Completed ❏

9. Inspect your work, clean up the area, and return all tools   Completed ❏
    and materials to their assigned places.

Instructor's Initials:_____

Date: _____

Job Practice 36 Review ▬▬▬▬▬▬▬▬▬▬▬▬▬▬

Ater completing this job successfully, answer the following questions correctly:

1. What is the function of the collar joint in a composite wall?_____

_____

_____

_____

_____

2. What is the proper name for 4″ × 8″ × 16″ concrete blocks?_____

_____

3. What tool was recommended for parging the blocks on the inner wythe adjacent to the outer wythe?

_____

4. About how far apart were the Z ties placed? _____

_____

5. What tool was used to strike the horizontal joints? _____

_____

Score: _____

Job Practice 37
Cleaning Concrete Block Masonry

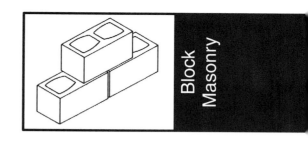

Name_____

Date_____

Instructor_____

Period _____

Objective

After completing this job you will be able to clean concrete block masonry using proper technique.

Equipment

To complete this job you will need the following tools and materials:

- ❖ Eye and hand protection
- ❖ Mason's trowel
- ❖ Chisel or putty knife
- ❖ Piece of concrete block
- ❖ Commercial cleaning agent

Recommended Procedure

Study the appropriate section in Chapter 11 (Laying Block) before starting this job. Concrete block walls are not cleaned with acid to remove mortar smears or droppings. Therefore, care must be taken to keep the wall surface clean during construction.

1. Allow any mortar droppings that stick to the wall to dry and harden before attempting to remove them.   Completed ❑

2. Remove large particles of dry mortar with a trowel, chisel, or putty knife. If you attempt to remove wet mortar, it will most likely smear into the surface of the block and become permanent.   Completed ❑

3. Using a piece of concrete block, rub the wall to remove practically all of the mortar.   Completed ❑

4. If further cleaning is necessary, then a commercial cleaning agent such as a detergent may be used. Be sure to follow the manufacturer's directions and try out the product on a small section of the wall to check the results.   Completed ☐

Instructor's Initials:_____

Date: _____

Job Practice 37 Review

After completing this job successfully, answer the following questions correctly:

1. Why do you suppose concrete block walls are not cleaned with acid? _____

_____

_____

_____

2. When should you try to remove any mortar droppings that stick to the wall? _____

_____

3. How did you remove large particles from the wall? _____

_____

4. After removing hardened particles from the wall, what is the next step?_____

_____

_____

5. If a wall still has smears after the recommended cleaning procedure has been followed, then what can you do? _____

_____

_____

Score: _____

Job Practice **38**
Handling Stone

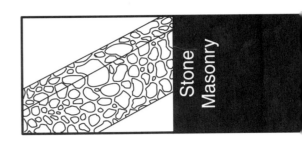

Name_____

Date_____

Instructor _____

Period _____

Objective ▰▰▰▰▰▰▰▰▰▰▰▰▰▰▰▰▰▰▰▰▰▰▰▰▰▰▰▰▰▰▰▰

After completing this job you will be able to handle stone using proper technique.

Equipment ▰▰▰▰▰▰▰▰▰▰▰▰▰▰▰▰▰▰▰▰▰▰▰▰▰▰▰▰▰▰▰▰

To complete this job you will need the following tools and materials:

- ❖ Steel-toed shoes and leather gloves
- ❖ Pry bar
- ❖ Safety glasses or goggles
- ❖ Mason's hammer
- ❖ Sledgehammer
- ❖ Chisel
- ❖ Variety of stone samples

Recommended Procedure ▰▰▰▰▰▰▰▰▰▰▰▰▰▰▰▰▰▰▰▰▰▰▰

Study the appropriate section of Chapter 12 (Stone Masonry) before starting this job.

Field stone

Stone used for rubble or roughly squared stonework will most likely be field stone in the sizes and shapes as they are found in fields and streams. The stone will be varied also as to type of stone in the load. A skilled stonemason will know which ones can be split easily and which shapes will look best in various locations in the wall. Try to learn from your experience and work with an experienced person to discover the *tricks of the trade*. For example, bedding is visible in most sedimentary stones and an experienced mason will know just where to strike the stone to split it.

1. Keep the pile of stone close to where you are working, but clear of the work area. If the source of stone is too far away, you will spend most of your time running back and forth. If it is too close, you won't have any room to work, and may fall over the stones. Spread out the stones and look them over to see what you have.

Completed ☐

2. Form a particular pattern in your mind before you begin setting stone. The pattern should take into consideration the size, shape, and type of stone you have to work with. If all the stones are round and smooth, don't plan a pattern that requires cutting and trimming every stone. If you plan to build a polygonal stone pattern, then order broken stone that already has the basic shapes needed. Study the basic patterns shown in Illustration 38-1.   Completed ❑

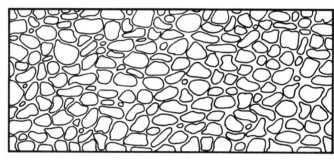

No. 1 Uncoursed Field Stone Rough or Common Rubble

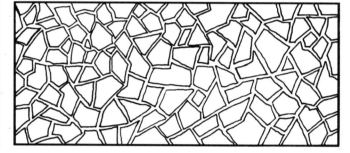

No. 2 Uncoursed Cobweb or Polygonal Stone

No. 3 Uncoursed and Roughly Squared

No. 4 Coursed and Roughly Squared Stone

Illustration 38-1. Representative stone patterns that use field stones.

3. Pick out a large stone to break into smaller pieces for an uncoursed and roughly squared stone pattern. Do not try to lift large stones by yourself. Remember that a cubic foot of granite weighs about 170 lbs. Use pry bars to move large stones.   Completed ❑

 Warning! Be sure to wear protective clothing when working with stone safety glasses or goggles, steel-toed shoes, and heavy leather gloves.

4. Examine the stone that has been selected to see if it has any potential break lines. Try to visualize where it might break. Strike it with your mason's hammer to see the results. If it refuses to break, use a larger hammer or sledgehammer.   Completed ❑

5. Next, try to remove an unwanted protuberance on a flat side of a stone with a chisel. Crush or powder a point on a stone with the mason's hammer. The purpose of this job is to get the feel of working with rubble stone.   Completed ❑

Name_____

Ashlar, trimmings, and panels

Cut stone in the form of trimmings, ashlar, or panels must be handled carefully to prevent breakage, staining, or chipping. This stone is delivered to the job site already cut, dressed, and finished to precise specifications for a particular job. The following suggestions should be helpful in handling this type of stone. See Illustration 38-2.

1. Examine several pieces of cut stone to determine the condition of each piece. Make note of chips, scratches, broken pieces, or discolored stone.   Completed ❑

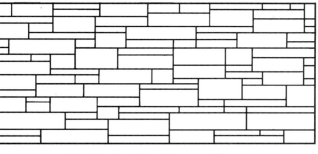

No. 5 Random, Broken Course and Range

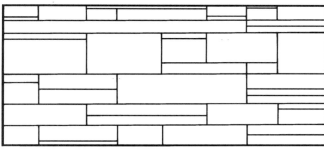

No. 6 Coursed Broken Bond, Broken Range Stone

Illustration 38-2. Ashlar stone patterns.

2. Handle this stone as you would any other material that you don't want to chip or scratch. Don't slide it on a rough surface. Store it on sturdy skids or timbers in a dry place.   Completed ❑

3. Lean smooth-finished stones face-to-face and back-to-back. Textured finishes should be separated with spacers. Be careful not to bump stones.   Completed ❑

4. Examine large stone panels to see if they have lifting holes. Discuss safety procedures when lifting large stone panels with your instructor. Estimate the weight of a large panel by figuring its volume and weight per cubic foot.   Completed ❑

5. Become familiar with the various types of stone by name and application. Get to know your material.   Completed ❑

Instructor's Initials:_____

Date: _____

Job Practice 38 Review ▬▬▬▬▬▬▬▬▬▬▬▬▬▬▬▬▬▬▬▬▬▬▬▬▬▬

After completing this job successfully, answer the following questions correctly:

1. What kind of stone is generally used for rubble or roughly squared stone work? _____
   _____

2. In what type of stones is bedding usually visible? _____
   _____

3. What is the problem with keeping your source of stone too close to where you are building the wall?
   _____
   _____
   _____

4. Once the stone is delivered, what should you do first? _____
   _____
   _____
   _____

5. How did you remove small knobs or protuberances from stones? _____
   _____

6. How should textured panels be stacked?_____
   _____
   _____

Score: _____

Job Practice **39**
Forming Mortar Joints in Stone Masonry

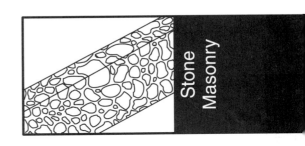

Stone Masonry

Name_____

Date_____

Instructor _____

Period _____

Objective

After completing this job, you will be able to form mortar joints in stone masonry using proper technique.

Equipment

To complete this job you will need the following tools and materials:

❖ Stonemason's tools

❖ Mortar

❖ Wood wedges

❖ Assortment of broken stone pieces

❖ Assortment of cut stone pieces

❖ Narrow caulking trowel

Recommended Procedure

Study the appropriate section of Chapter 12 (Stone Masonry) before starting this job.

Joints in stone masonry are generally set with mortar. Joints in stone panel construction may be mortar or other materials. Whenever mortar is used, it should be a nonstaining type designed for the specific application. A mix of 1 part nonstaining cement, 1 part hydrated lime, and 6 parts clean, sharp, washed sand is recommended.

The width of the mortar joints will have a profound effect on the finished appearance of the stone construction. The most frequent error is to allow the mortar joints to become too wide, especially with the use of rubble or polygonal stones. Stones should be cut to fit with mortar joints that are 1/2″ for rough work and 3/8″ for ashlar. Use a narrow caulking trowel for filling narrow spaces and working mortar into crevices.

This job will provide the opportunity to form mortar joints using polygonal stone.

See Illustration 39-1 to form a picture in your mind of the basic layout to be attempted in this job.

Illustration 39-1. Polygonal stonework.

1. Select a vertical masonry or wood backing about 24″ × 36″ in size. You will lay your stonework against it.

   Completed ☐

2. Select an assortment of polygonal shaped stones of various sizes, but not over one square foot in area.

   Completed ☐

3. Arrange them in a pleasing pattern on the floor. You might have to chip away some part of a stone to make it fit, but try to find pieces that naturally fit together.

   Completed ☐

4. When you have several pieces selected that will cover about four square feet, mix some mortar (not too thin) and lay a mortar bed long enough for two or three of the larger stones. Larger stones are generally placed at the bottom of a wall.

   Completed ☐

5. Set the base stones in the mortar bed and against the backup. If the stones are not stable, or too much mortar squeezes out, place one or two wood wedges under each stone. Remember to keep narrow mortar joints.

   Completed ☐

6. Continue along the base until the width is completed. Remove excess mortar and try to keep it off the face of the stones.

   Completed ☐

7. Pick up the next stone to be placed and see how it fits the space intended for it. You may have to try several stones to get just the right fit.

   Completed ☐

8. When you are sure the stone will fit properly, lay a bed of mortar on the stone already in place and set this stone. Remove excess mortar and insert wedges if needed.

   Completed ☐

9. Continue the process until you have covered the space. Be very careful around the structure, because it may fall very easily.

   Completed ☐

Name_____

0. When the mortar has hardened some, carefully rake out some mortar between the stones until the joint is about 1″ deep. You may remove some of the wedges. Or if your work was very good, tool the joints with a short jointer. Carefully add mortar with the narrow caulking trowel where it is needed to replace the mortar removed earlier.   Completed ❏

1. When the mortar has hardened, remove the wedges, and brush the stone to remove mortar splatters. Fill any holes left when the wedges were removed.   Completed ❏

2. Inspect your work to see how your mortar joints look. Clean up the area and return the tools and materials to their assigned places.   Completed ❏

Instructor's Initials:_____

Date: _____

Job Practice 39 Review

After completing this job successfully, answer the following questions correctly:

1. What is the recommended mortar mix for stone masonry? _____

_____

_____

_____

2. What is the most frequent error in forming mortar joints in stone masonry?_____

_____

3. How did you prevent large stones from squeezing out too much mortar?_____

_____

_____

4. What is the general approach to shaping polygonal stone? _____

_____

_____

5. What tool is generally used to point stonework? _____

_____

_____

Score: _____

Job Practice 40
Splitting, Shaping, and Cutting Stone for Stone Masonry Work

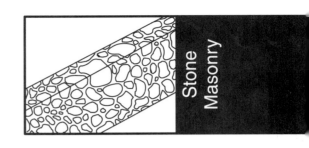

Stone Masonry

Name_____

Date_____

Instructor _____

Period _____

Objective

After completing this job you will be able to split, shape, and cut stone for stone masonry work using proper technique.

Equipment

To complete this job you will need the following tools and materials:

- ❖ Stonemason's tools
- ❖ Stonemason's hammer
- ❖ Sledgehammer
- ❖ Pry bar
- ❖ Steel wedges
- ❖ Electric drill (optional)
- ❖ Stonemason's chisel
- ❖ Safety glasses and other protective gear

Recommended Procedure

Study the appropriate section of Chapter 12 (Stone Masonry) before starting this job. Splitting stone takes some practice and sharp observation to achieve the desired results in a consistent manner.

1. To split a stone that has a stratified (layered) structure, mark a line along the grain, then chip on the line with the chisel end of your mason's hammer until a crack begins to develop.

Completed ☐

2. Widen the crack slowly by driving wedges into the crack at several points. If it is a very large stone, a pry bar may be needed to finish prying it apart. Force it apart.   Completed ❏

3. Select a large stone such as granite that is not stratified. These stones are difficult to split, but it is possible. Begin by drilling holes with the narrow bladed chisel or power drill about 6″ apart along the line where you wish the stone to split.   Completed ❏

4. Drive thin wedges into the holes. Keep up the process until the stone splits.   Completed ❏

5. Select a split stone and shape it with your mason's hammer. Also try the stonemason's chisel. Be sure you are wearing safety glasses.   Completed ❏

6. Ask for a demonstration on using the power masonry saw. It will be used to cut a piece of ashlar to a particular dimension. Never use any equipment until the instructor gives his/her approval. You must practice safety.   Completed ❏

7. Select a piece of cut stone and plan a cut across the end. Hold it firmly against the fence and slowly make a cut towards you. When the cut is finished return the saw to the starting position. Examine your cut. Make another cut to get the feel for the saw. Never try to cut large panels or pieces too big for the saw.   Completed ❏

Instructor's Initials:_____

Date: _____

Job Practice 40 Review

After completing this job successfully, answer the following questions correctly:

1. Briefly, what is the procedure for splitting a stone that has a stratified structure?_____

_____

_____

_____

_____

2. What is the recommended procedure for splitting a stone that is not stratified?_____

_____

_____

_____

_____

Name_____

3. What personal safety equipment is recommended for working with stone? _____

_____

_____

4. What direction is the cut made when using the power masonry saw? _____

_____

5. How should a piece of stone be held when cutting with the masonry saw? _____

_____

Score: _____

Job Practice **41**
Setting a Random Rubble Stone Veneer Wall

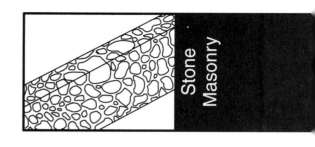

Stone Masonry

Name_____

Date_____

Instructor_____

Period _____

Objective

After completing this job you will be able to set a random rubble stone veneer wall using proper technique.

Equipment

To complete this job you will need the following tools and materials:

- ❖ Stonemason's tools
- ❖ Mortar
- ❖ Typical safety equipment
- ❖ Existing wall—masonry or frame
- ❖ Supply of rubble stone
- ❖ Corrugated ties
- ❖ Piece of chalk
- ❖ Bucket of water and sponge

Recommended Procedure

Study the appropriate section in Chapter 12 (Stone Masonry) before starting this job. This job requires an existing wall to receive the stone veneer. The back-up wall may be masonry or frame, but should already have, or provide for the attachment of flexible ties or corrugated fasteners. The wall area should be at least 4' wide by 4' high. Illustration 41-1 shows what the wall should look like when completed.

Illustration 41-1. Random rubble stonework with uniform mortar joints.

1. Arrange your work area and spread out the stone so that each one may be examined for shape, texture, or other characteristics. This stone will most likely vary in size from 6″ to 18″.

Completed ▢

2. Mix enough mortar to last for 1 hour of work. Use it up before it begins to set. Be sure to use a nonstaining mortar. Mix 1 part nonstaining cement, 1 part hydrated lime, and 6 parts clean, sharp, washed sand. A comparable manufactured mortar cement can also be used.

Completed ▢

3. Select several larger stones for the bed course and place them into position dry. With a piece of chalk, mark them for trimming.

Stones should be placed in as natural a position as possible. Have a pattern or special effect in mind as you select and place stones together. Do not use too many varieties and keep textures relatively uniform. Stone veneer is generally 4″ to 8″ thick depending on the method of bonding and construction specifications. See Illustration 41-2.

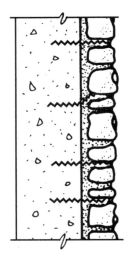

4″—8″ Stone Tied To Concrete Backing Using Wall Ties

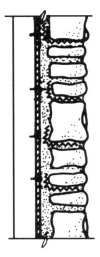

4″—8″ Stone Tied To Frame Construction. Use Wood Sheathing And W.P. Felt Or W.P. Sheathing Board

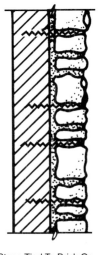

4″—8″ Stone Tied To Brick Or Block Masonry, Provide 1″–2″ ▲ Space Or Slush Fill Voids

Illustration 41-2. Stone veneer sections.

Name_____

Large stones must be split so that they will meet these requirements. A sledgehammer may be used for splitting large stones.

Completed ❑

4. Trim each stone as you are ready to place it in the wall. Each stone should be thoroughly cleaned on all exposed surfaces by washing with a brush and soap powder, followed by a thorough drenching with clean water.

Completed ❑

⚠ **Warning!** Be careful of flying chips! Wear safety glasses.

5. Place each trimmed stone in its proper location in the wall and check for proper fit. When you are satisfied with the result, proceed to the next step.

Completed ❑

6. Using the trowel, lay a generous full bed of mortar for the trimmed stones and place them into position.

Completed ❑

7. Fill in the spaces between the stones with mortar. A narrow caulking trowel works well for filling narrow spaces and working the mortar into crevices. See Illustration 41-3. Joints should be about 1/2″ for rough work such as this. Sponge the stone free of mortar along the joints as the work progresses.

Completed ❑

Illustration 41-3. Narrow caulking trowel.

8. Remove excess mortar from the stone with the trowel and strike the joint. Joints can be tooled when initial set has occurred. If desired, they can be raked out 1″ deeper and pointed later with mortar.

Completed ❑

9. Trim other stones for the deeper bed course and fit them into place using the same procedure.

10. Bend corrugated metal ties into place for successive courses of stone. All ties must be noncorrosive. Use extra ties at all corners and large stones when possible.

Lead, plastic, or wood pads the thickness of mortar joints, should be placed under heavy stones to avoid squeezing mortar out. See Illustration 41-4. Remove the pads after the mortar has set, then fill the holes. Heavy stones or projecting courses should not be set until mortar in courses below has hardened sufficiently to avoid squeezing.

Illustration 41-4. Wood pads support heavy stones.

11. Using the above procedure, lay the remaining stones until the wall is the desired height. Work from the corners toward the middle as in laying any masonry wall.

A mason's line and level may be used to keep the wall straight and plumb. (If the structure is inclined or tapered as in many chimneys, then a mason's line should be used to keep the edge straight and moving in the proper direction.

The masonry should be protected at all times from rain and masonry droppings. And, adequate protection must be provided during cold weather construction.

12. When the wall is completed, it may be scrubbed with a fiber brush and clean water. The stone should be clean and free of mortar.

Name_____

Strong acid compounds generally should not be used as they may burn and discolor certain types of stone, such as limestone. Waterproofing may be used. Use a nonstaining asphalt emulsion, vinyl lacquer, cement base masonry waterproofing, stearate, or other approved material.

Completed ❑

3. Inspect your work, clean up the area, and return all tools and materials to their assigned places.

Completed ❑

Instructor's Initials:_____

Date: _____

Job Practice 41 Review ■■■■■■■■■■■■■■■■■■■■■■■■■■

After completing this job successfully, answer the following questions correctly:

1. Rubble stone is available in a wide variety of sizes and any load will most likely be composed of stones of many sizes. Is there a general rule to follow in placing larger stones? _____

_____

_____

2. Is coursing possible in a rubble stone masonry wall? Why? _____

_____

_____

3. How does the strength of mortar bonds in a rubble stone wall compare with other types of stone walls? _____

_____

_____

4. What is the overall appearance or style communicated by a rubble stone wall?_____

_____

5. What type of metal tie is generally used to bond a rubble stone wall to its backup? _____

_____

6. How much mortar should you mix when placing stone masonry?_____

_____

Score: _____

Job Practice **42**

Building a Solid 12″ Thick Ashlar Stone Wall

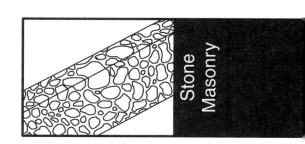

Stone Masonry

Name_____

Date_____

Instructor _____

Period _____

Objective

After completing this job you will be able to build a solid ashlar stone wall using proper technique.

Equipment

To complete this job you will need the following tools and materials:

- ❖ Stonemason's tools
- ❖ Mortar
- ❖ Typical safety equipment
- ❖ Supply of ashlar stone (variety of dimensions)
- ❖ Bucket of water and sponge

Recommended Procedure

Study the appropriate section in Chapter 12 (Stone Masonry) before beginning this job. Review Job Practice 41.

This job will provide the opportunity to build an ashlar stone wall section 12″ thick, 24″ high, and 60″ long. The material should include widths of 6″ and 12″ and various thicknesses and lengths. Illustration 42-1 shows the material.

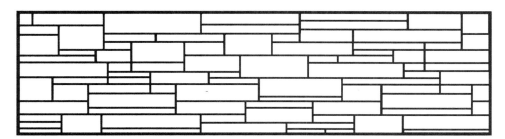

Illustration 42-1. Ashlar stone wall.

1. Collect the tools and materials needed for this job and arrange your work area. Be careful with the stone because it will chip easily.

   Completed ❏

2. Using the chalk line, snap a line to locate both sides of a wall 12″ thick and 60″ long. Be sure the ends are perpendicular to the face of the wall.

   Completed ❏

3. Lay out a pattern of stone on the floor to see how the various pieces can be assembled to provide the desired pattern. The lengths and thicknesses are usually designed to form a regular pattern with a standard mortar joint thickness.

   Completed ❏

4. When you have the pattern in your mind, mix some mortar and lay a full mortar bed for the base course for the front wythe of the wall. Be sure the chalk line is visible.

   Completed ❏

5. Set the first stone at one end of the wall. Level, plumb, and align the stone to be sure it is properly located. Check the mortar joint thickness to be sure it is 3/8″.

   Completed ❏

6. Set the remaining stones on the face wythe using an interesting variety of sizes. Follow your planned pattern. Remove excess mortar, level, and straightedge the wall.

   Completed ❏

7. Lay down a mortar bed for the back wythe of the wall. Be sure that some of the stones in this wythe are the same height as those opposite them so a bond stone (a stone that reaches across the total wall thickness) can be used at that point. Bond stones will tie the wythes together and provide strength and stability. Plan to insert a bond stone at regular intervals throughout the wall. Check each stone to be sure it is level and plumb. Any irregularity will be very visible in the finished wall.

   Completed ❏

8. Continue building the wall and working your pattern. Be sure to use full mortar joints and try to avoid getting mortar on the face of the stone.

   Completed ❏

9. When your wall has reached 24″ high, cap it off using 12″ wide pieces all the same thickness. Select a thickness that looks right in proportion to the size of stone used in the wall and its height and length.

   Completed ❏

10. Remove all excess mortar and tool the joints when the mortar has begun to harden. Remove mortar smears with a damp sponge. Rub the stone, not the mortar joints.

    Completed ❏

11. Inspect your work, clean up the area, and return your tools and materials to their assigned places.

    Completed ❏

Instructor's Initials:_____

Date: _____

Name_____

Job Practice 42 Review ▬▬▬▬▬▬▬▬▬▬▬▬▬▬

After completing this job successfully, answer the following questions correctly:

1. Define ashlar stone. _____
   _____

2. Is laying (setting) ashlar stone more similar to rubble stonework or laying bricks or blocks? _____
   _____

3. What lengths of ashlar stone are generally available?_____
   _____

4. What mortar thickness is commonly used with ashlar stone? _____
   _____

5. How many wythes did your 12" thick ashlar stone wall have?_____
   _____

6. How were the wythes tied together? _____
   _____

Score: _____

Job Practice 43
Setting a Limestone Panel

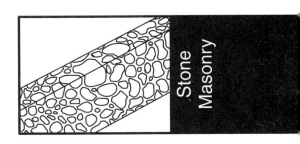

Stone Masonry

Name_____

Date_____

Instructor _____

Period _____

Objective

After completing this job you will be able to install a limestone panel using proper technique. ***This is a class project.***

Equipment

To complete this job you will need the following tools and materials:

- ❖ Stonemason's tools
- ❖ Mortar
- ❖ Typical safety equipment
- ❖ Limestone panels
- ❖ Lifting device and attachments
- ❖ Steel or concrete frame to receive the panels

Recommended Procedure

Study the appropriate section in Chapter 12 (Stone Masonry) before starting this job. This job involves setting a limestone panel on a steel or concrete frame which must be provided by the instructor. The Indiana Limestone Institute provides extensive procedures and criteria for the application of limestone panels. This job should be coordinated with their recommendations.

1. Study the construction drawings which include details of the anchoring system. Examine the panel and make note of provisions for attachment to the structural frame. Illustration 43-1 shows a typical attachment detail for a limestone panel.

Completed ☐

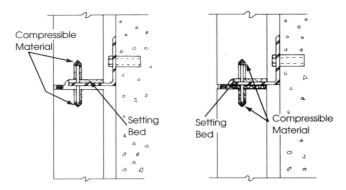

Illustration 43-1. Typical panel support detail.
(Indiana Limestone Institute)

2. Discuss with your instructor the method of lifting the stone panel into place. What safety precautions will be taken to protect you as well as prevent damage to the panel?   Completed ❏

3. Rehearse the process to be used to lift the panel and roles to be played by various members of the class. Be sure you have all the tools and materials at hand to complete the job once it is begun.   Completed ❏

 Warning! Hard hats are required.

4. Lift the panel and carefully guide it to its desired placement. Check alignment of all support pins or other attachments. Check the panel to be sure it is level, plumb, and securely attached to the building frame.   Completed ❏

5. Once the panel is securely anchored, review the process to discuss any problems or procedures that were unclear. Remove the panel and reinstall it again so that everyone has a chance to play the various roles in installing a large stone panel.   Completed ❏

6. Return the panel to storage and put away the tools and equipment used in this job.   Completed ❏

Instructor's Initials:_____

Date: _____

Name_____

Job Practice 43 Review ▬▬▬▬▬▬▬▬▬▬▬▬▬▬▬▬

After completing this job successfully, answer the following questions correctly:

1. How are limestone panels supported and attached to buildings? _____

   _____

   _____

   _____

2. How is a stone panel generally protected during the lifting and setting process? _____

   _____

   _____

   _____

   _____

3. How is setting a stone panel so different from other stonework? _____

   _____

   _____

   _____

   _____

4. Why must one be so careful in handling a stone panel? _____

   _____

5. What agency is considered the authority with respect to stone panel work? _____

   _____

Score: _____

Job Practice **44**
Pointing Cut Stone After Setting

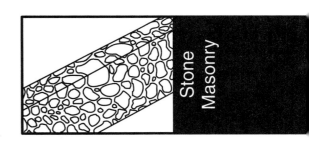

Stone Masonry

Name_____

Date_____

Instructor_____

Period _____

Objective

After completing this job you will be able to point cut stone using proper technique.

Equipment

To complete this job you will need the following tools and materials:

- ❖ Stonemason's tools
- ❖ Mortar
- ❖ Slicker
- ❖ Rake out jointer or skate wheel joint raker
- ❖ Stone assembly with mortar removed to 1″ deep

Recommended Procedure

Study the appropriate section in Chapter 12 (Stone Masonry) before starting this job.

Pointing cut stone after setting, rather than full bed setting and finishing in one operation, reduces a condition which tends to produce spalling and leakage. Shrinkage of the mortar bed will allow some settling since the mortar bed hardens from the face in. If set and pointed in one operation, the settling, combined with the hardened mortar at the face, can set up stresses on the edge of the stone. For this reason, it is best to set the stone and rake out the mortar to a depth of 1/2″ to 1 1/2″ for pointing with a mortar or sealant application at a later date. Pointing can be done in one, two, or three stages. This allows each stage to seal shrinkage cracks in the preceding stage and finally the concave tooled joint provides the maximum protection against leakage.

1. When the mortar has hardened sufficiently in a mortar joint, the skate wheel joint raker is used to remove the mortar to a depth of 1″. See Illustration 44-1.

Completed ☐

Illustration 44-1. The skate wheel joint raker.

2. Clean out the area where the mortar has been removed with the skate wheel joint raker. Use a brush or compressed air. The joint area must be clean of debris.   Completed ❑

3. Mix up a small quantity of mortar and apply about a 1/2" thick layer of mortar to the existing joint. Use a slicker to apply the mortar between the pieces of cut stone. Press the mortar into place so that it makes a good bond.   Completed ❑

4. When the previous application of mortar has hardened, then the next (in this case, the last) application may be started. Fill the mortar joint with new mortar, again using the slicker or narrow pointing trowel. The mortar should be flush with the surface of the stone units.   Completed ❑

5. When the mortar is thumbprint hard, tool the joints in the regular fashion. Remove tags and brush the stone to remove any mortar droppings. Sponge the stone to further clean the surface. Do not sponge the mortar joints.   Completed ❑

6. A commercial sealer may be applied if desired. Follow the manufacturer's instructions of a sealer if used.   Completed ❑

7. Inspect your work, clean up the area, and return tools and materials to their assigned places.   Completed ❑

Instructor's Initials:_____

Date: _____

Name_____

Job Practice 44 Review ▬▬▬▬▬▬▬▬▬

After completing this job successfully, answer the following questions correctly:

1. What is the purpose in pointing cut stone? _____

   _____

2. How deep is the mortar generally raked out for pointing? _____

   _____

3. How many stages are generally used to point cut stone after setting? _____

   _____

4. What tool is most often used to rake out the mortar for pointing?_____

   _____

5. What tool is used to add new mortar to the joint? _____

   _____

6. What is the purpose of applying a commercial sealer to cut stone? _____

   _____

Score: _____

Job Practice 45
Cleaning New Stone Masonry

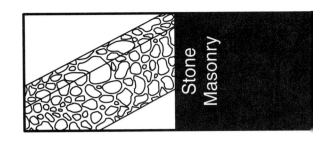

Stone Masonry

Name_____

Date_____

Instructor _____

Period _____

Objective

After completing the job you will be able to clean new stone masonry using proper technique.

Equipment

To complete this job you will need the following tools and materials:

❖ Eye and skin protection

❖ Stiff fiber brush

❖ Bucket and water

❖ Detergent

❖ Rinsing water (under pressure)

Recommended Procedure

Study the appropriate section in Chapter 12 (Stone Masonry) before starting this job.

The finished appearance of a stone masonry wall depends not only on the skill used in setting the units but on the cleaning procedure as well. The appearance of a masonry structure may be ruined by improper cleaning. In many instances, the damage caused by faulty cleaning techniques or the use of the wrong cleaning agent cannot be repaired. All cleaning should be applied to a sample test area of approximately 20 sq. ft.

Always take precautions to protect the stone from water, dirt, and mortar splatter as the work progresses. Cover the wall with a waterproof membrane at the end of each workday. Careful workmanship should be practiced to prevent excessive mortar droppings.

Acids, wire brushes, and sandblasting are usually not permitted on stonework. Strong acid compounds used for cleaning brick will burn and discolor many types of stone. Machine cleaning processes should be approved by the supplier before using.

1. Brush off the stone with a stiff fiber brush to remove any loose dirt or mortar. The mortar should be cured at this point. Cleaning uncured mortar can cause damage and spread scum over the stone surfaces.

Completed ❑

2. Using a stiff fiber brush and clean water, scrub the wall. Concentrate on the stone, not on the mortar joints.   **Completed** ☐

3. If stains are difficult to remove, use soapy water and then rinse with clear water. If the stonework has been kept clean by sponging during construction, the final cleaning will be much easier.   **Completed** ☐

4. Look over the wall to see if any spots have been missed. Clean these spots.   **Completed** ☐

5. Return tools and materials to their assigned places.   **Completed** ☐

Instructor's Initials:_____

Date: _____

Job Practice 45 Review

After completing this job successfully, answer the following questions correctly.

1. What kind of personal safety protection is recommended when cleaning new stone masonry?_____

   _____

2. How can improper cleaning ruin a stone masonry job?_____

   _____

3. Cleaning a test area of stone is recommended in an obscure area to be sure the cleaning agent is compatible with the stone. How large an area is recommended and how long do you wait to see the results? _____

   _____

   _____

4. What cleaning processes are generally not permitted on stone? _____

   _____

   _____

5. What is the possible effect of cleaning uncured mortar? _____

   _____

   _____

Score: _____

Job Practice **46**
Applying Manufactured Stone to a Backup

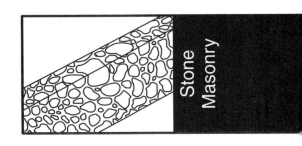

Stone Masonry

Objective

After completing this job you will be able to apply manufactured stone to a backup using proper technique.

Equipment

To complete this job you will need the following tools and materials:

- ❖ Plasterer's trowel
- ❖ Mason's trowel
- ❖ Slick or narrow pointing trowel
- ❖ Stiff bristle brush
- ❖ Hatchet
- ❖ Grout bag

Recommended Procedure

Study the appropriate section in Chapter 7 (Stone) before starting this job.

Manufactured stone is a simulated stone veneer made from lightweight concrete. It is colorfast, weatherproof, and has the look and feel of natural stone. Manufactured stone may be applied directly to a base coat of stucco, concrete block, brick, concrete, or any masonry surface that has not been treated or sealed and which is rough enough to provide a good mechanical bond. Illustration 46-1 shows a typical application.

Illustration 46-1. Applying manufactured stone to a masonry wall.

1. Preparing the surface. If the surface is clean (unpainted, unsealed, or untreated) brick, block, or concrete the stone may be applied directly to the surface. On all other surfaces, metal lath must be applied first. Nail or staple the lath six inches on center. Use a vapor barrier such as building felt under the lath on outside applications.

Completed ❑

2. Applying the scratch coat. A thin scratch coat of mortar is generally applied and allowed to set prior to installing the stone. Mortar for this operation can be mixed by combining masonry cement and sand or regular Portland cement, lime, and sand. The consistency should not be too thin or too dry—just average. This mortar can be used for the scratch coat, for applying the stone, and grouting the joints. Apply the scratch coat with a plasterer's trowel.

Completed ❑

3. Applying mortar to the stone. Lay out the stone near the work area and become familiar with the various shapes and sizes. When you are ready to begin, select a stone and apply a 1/2" thick, even layer of mortar to the back of the stone. Use the mason's trowel for this operation.

Completed ❑

4. Applying the stone. Press the stone firmly into place on the wall surface so that the mortar behind the stone squeezes out around all sides. Using a gentle wiggling action while applying the stone will ensure a good bond. Application of manufactured stone is usually begun at the top to help keep the stone clean during construction. Install corner stones first to make fitting easier. Keep the mortar joints tight and uniform.

Completed ❑

Name_____

5. Trimming the stone. When necessary, manufactured stone can be cut and shaped with a hatchet, brick trowel, or nippers to form special sizes and shapes for better fitting. Try to position stones on the wall so cut edges will not show. Trim a stone to fit a particular spot.

Completed ❑

6. Grouting the joints. After all the stone has been applied to the surface, fill a grout bag with mortar. Partially fill the joints between the stones with mortar. Be sure to cover broken stone edges with mortar.

Completed ❑

7. Striking the joints. When the mortar joints have hardened sufficiently, use a wood or metal striking tool to rake out the excess mortar to the desired depth and at the same time to force the mortar into the joints to seal the joint edges.

Completed ❑

8. Brushing. Brush the mortar joints with a stiff bristle brush to smooth them and clean away any loose mortar. Remove mortar spots from the face of the stone.

Completed ❑

9. Completion. Use a high quality waterproofing sealer on the surface. This will help keep the surface clean.

Completed ❑

10. Inspect your work, clean up the area, and return all tools and materials to their assigned places.

Completed ❑

Instructor's Initials:_____

Date: _____

Job Practice 46 Review

After completing this job successfully, answer the following questions correctly:

1. What kind of concrete is used to make manufactured stone? _____

_____

2. What kinds of bases are suitable for the application of manufactured stone?_____

_____

_____

_____

_____

3. What is a *scratch coat*? _____

_____

_____

_____

4. What tool is used to apply a scratch coat? _____

_____

5. What mason's tool may be used to cut manufactured stone? _____

_____

6. When applying manufactured stone, should you start at the top or bottom of the wall? Why? _____

_____

_____

Score: _____

Job Practice 47
Measuring Concrete Materials

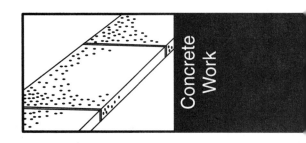

Concrete Work

Name_____

Date_____

Instructor _____

Period _____

Objective

After completing this job you will be able to measure concrete materials using proper technique.

Equipment

To complete this job you will need the following tools and materials:

❖ Scale to weigh materials

❖ One cubic foot box

❖ Dry and moist sand

❖ Unopened bag of cement

❖ Eye and hand protection

Recommended Procedure

Study the appropriate section in Chapter 14 (Concrete Materials and Applications) before starting this job. The ingredients in each batch of concrete must be measured accurately if uniform batches of proper proportions and consistency are to be produced. The problem of varying amounts of moisture in the aggregate must be taken into account if accurate control is to be obtained.

1. **Measuring cement.** If bagged cement is used, the batches should be of such a size that only full bags are used. If this is not possible, then the proper amount should be weighed out each time. Volume is not an accurate method of measuring cement. Bulk cement (not bagged) should always be weighed for each batch. Weight a bag of Portland Type I cement to see how much it weighs and record the weight.

Completed ❏

2. **Measuring water.** The effects of the water-cement ratio on the qualities of concrete make it just as necessary to measure accurately the water used as any other materials. Water is measured in gallons and any method that will ensure accuracy is acceptable. (One gallon of water weighs 8.33 lbs.) Fill a five gallon bucket, weigh it, and record the weight.   Completed ❏

3. **Measuring aggregates.** Measurement of aggregates by weight is the recommended practice and should be required on all jobs that require a high degree of consistency in each batch. Measurement of fine aggregate (sand) by volume is not accurate because a small amount of moisture is nearly always present. This moisture causes the fine aggregate to bulk or fluff up. The degree of bulking depends on the amount of moisture present and the fineness of the sand. A fine sand with a 5% moisture content will increase in volume about 40% above its dry volume. Weigh a cubic foot of very dry sand and a cubic foot of moist sand. Compare their weights. Use a measuring box.   Completed ❏

4. Compare the results of measuring by volume and measuring by weight. Remember these comparisons.   Completed ❏

5. Clean up the area and return tools and materials to their assigned places.   Completed ❏

Instructor's Initials:_____

Date: _____

Job Practice 47 Review ▬▬▬▬▬▬▬▬▬▬▬▬▬▬▬

After completing this job successfully, answer the following questions correctly:

1. Many workers fill the concrete mixer with so many shovels of sand, cement, and coarse aggregate. Why is this practice not recommended? _____

   _____

2. Why is volume not an accurate method of measuring cement? _____

   _____

3. How much does one gallon of water weigh? _____

   _____

4. About how much does fine sand increase in volume when it has a 5% moisture content? _____

   _____

5. How should the water to be used in a batch of concrete be measured?_____

   _____

   _____

Score: _____

Job Practice **48**
Mixing Concrete with a Power Mixer

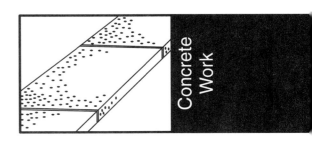

Concrete Work

Name_____

Date_____

Instructor _____

Period _____

Objective

After completing this job you will be able to mix concrete in a power mixer using proper technique.

Equipment

To complete this job you will need the following tools and materials:

- ❖ Power cement mixer
- ❖ Shovel
- ❖ Measuring box or scales
- ❖ Five gallon bucket
- ❖ Bag of Type I cement
- ❖ Source of dry sand
- ❖ Crushed stone
- ❖ Source of water
- ❖ Eye protection

Recommended Procedure

Study the appropriate section in Chapter 14 (Concrete Materials and Applications) before starting this job.

All concrete should be mixed thoroughly until it is uniform in appearance and all ingredients are uniformly distributed. The mixing time will depend on several factors: the speed of the machine, the size of the batch, and the condition of the mixer. Generally, the mixing time should be at least one minute for mixtures up to 1 cu. yd. with an increase of 15 seconds for each 1/2 cu. yd. or fraction thereof. Mixing time should be measured from the time all materials are in the mixer. Generally, about 10% of the mixing water is placed in the mixer before the aggregate and cement are added. Water should then be added uniformly along with the dry materials. The last 10% of the water is added after all the dry materials are added.

1. Assemble all of the materials and tools needed for this job.
   Arrange your work space.   Completed ❑

2. Check the mixer to be sure it is clean and in good working order. Start the mixer and add about one-tenth of the water anticipated for a four cubic foot batch. (A typical batch proportion is 1:2:3, one part cement, 2 parts sand, and 3 parts crushed stone.) The amount of water needed for this mix is about 1/2 gal./cu. ft. of cement.   Completed ☐

3. Add the sand and cement in proper amounts to the mixer. Add all but about 10% of the water. Mark the time.   Completed ☐

4. Mix the ingredients for 15 seconds. Stop the mixer and examine the results. Decide whether or not to add any more water. Remember that concrete should only be as wet as is necessary to place and finish it. The more water, the weaker the hardened product.   Completed ☐

5. If more water is added, mix for another 5 seconds.   Completed ☐

Go to Job 49 and perform a slump test on the plastic concrete.

Instructor's Initials:_____

Date: _____

Job Practice 48 Review ▰▰▰▰▰▰▰▰▰▰▰▰▰▰▰▰

After completing this job successfully, answer the following questions correctly:

1. What is the intended use of Type I cement? _____

_____

_____

2. Name the factors that mixing time is dependent upon.

_____

3. What is the recommended mixing time for a one cubic yard batch? _____

_____

4. What is a typical batch proportion of cement to sand to large aggregate? _____

_____

5. What is the effect on hardened concrete if too much water was used in the mixing process? _____

_____

6. What is the normal curing time of concrete in days?_____

_____

Score: _____

Job Practice 49

Performing a Slump Test on Plastic Concrete

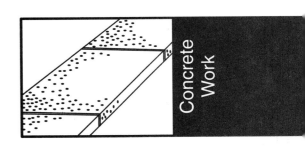

Concrete Work

Name_____

Date_____

Instructor _____

Period _____

Objective

After completing this job you will be able to perform a standard slump test on plastic concrete using proper technique.

Equipment

To complete this job you will need the following tools and materials:

❖ Eye protection

❖ Standard slump cone

❖ Metal rod 24″ long by 5/8″ in diameter

❖ Mason's trowel

❖ Five gallon bucket with water

❖ Measuring tape or folding rule

Recommended Procedure

Study the appropriate section in Chapter 14 (Concrete Materials and Applications) before starting this job.

The mix consistency or degree of stiffness of plastic concrete is called slump. Slump is measured in inches. Very fluid (wet) mixes are called high-slump concrete while stiff (dry) mixes are called low-slump concrete. Slump is related primarily to water-cement ratio. Generally, a low-slump concrete will produce a better concrete product. See Illustration 49-1.

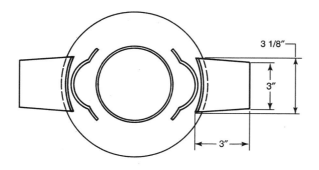

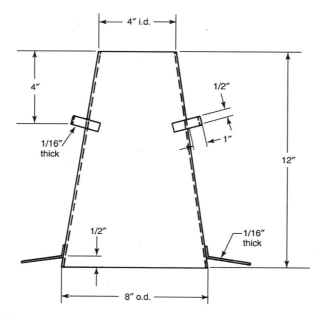

Illustration 49-1. Typical sheet metal slump cone.

1. Assemble the tools and materials needed for this job. Set up a work area close to the concrete mixer.

Completed ❑

2. Place the slump cone on a clean, dry, and level surface. Fill it one third full of concrete from the freshly mixed batch. The sample should be representative of the total batch. Use the mason's trowel or shovel to take the sample.

Completed ❑

3. Using the 24" metal rod, rod the concrete in the cone 25 times. Move the rod to different locations so that the concrete is thoroughly mixed.

Completed ❑

4. Remove the rod and add more concrete until the cone is 2/3 full. Rod the concrete 25 more times with the rod penetrating to the bottom.

Completed ❑

5. Fill the cone with concrete. Rake off the top with the rod until it is level and then rod 25 more times as before.

Completed ❑

Name_____

6. Remove the rod, remove the cone, and set it beside the concrete. Immediately measure the slump by placing the rod across the top of the cone and over the concrete. Measure the distance from the bottom of the rod to the top of the concrete. This distance is the slump rating for the batch.   Completed ❑

7. Clean up the tools and the area and return all tools and equipment to their assigned places. Be sure to remove all concrete from the mixer.   Completed ❑

Instructor's Initials:_____

Date: _____

Job Practice 49 Review ▬▬▬▬▬▬▬▬▬▬▬▬▬▬▬

After completing this job successfully, answer the following questions correctly:

1. Define the term *slump.* _____
   _____
   _____

2. Describe the difference between concrete that has a high slump and concrete that has a low slump.
   _____
   _____

3. Why is concrete rodded so many times when filling a metal slump cone? _____
   _____
   _____

4. What are the dimensions of the rod that is used in a slump test?_____
   _____
   _____

5. How is the measurement made to determine the slump of a concrete batch? _____
   _____
   _____
   _____
   _____

Score: _____

Job Practice **50**
Placing Concrete in a Slab Form

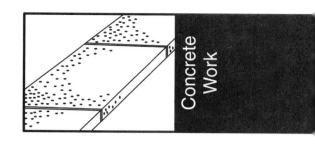

Concrete Work

Name_____

Date_____

Instructor_____

Period_____

Objective

After completing this job you will be able to place concrete in a slab form using proper technique.

Equipment

To complete this job you will need the following tools and materials:

- ❖ Prepared form ready for concrete
- ❖ Protective clothing
- ❖ Shovel
- ❖ Rake

Recommended Procedure

Study the appropriate section in Chapter 16 (Concrete Flatwork and Formed Shapes) before starting this job.

Concrete is moved about for placing by many methods. Some of the most popular methods include chutes, push buggies, buckets handled by cranes, wheelbarrows, and pumping through pipes. The method used to move the concrete is not important so long as it does not restrict the desired consistency of the concrete. Consistency should be governed by placing conditions and the application.

This job is designed to provide experience in placing concrete in a typical form designed to cast a flat slab. The size is not important, but a section of sidewalk (3′ × 6′) would be adequate.

1. Assemble the tools and materials needed for this job. Wear protective clothing such as safety glasses, hard hat, gloves, and rubber boots if the slab is too large to work from the edges.

Completed ☐

2. Check the form and subgrade to be sure everything is ready for the concrete. Once the concrete arrives, you will not have time to do these things. Forms should be in place and level. The subgrade should be smooth and moist. Moistening the subgrade prevents the rapid loss of water from the concrete when flatwork is being placed. This is especially important in hot weather. Refer to Illustration 50-1.

Completed ☐

Illustration 50-1. Form ready for concrete.

3. If reinforcing steel is to be used in the slab, it should be in place. Also, it should be clean and free of loose rust or scale. No hardened mortar or concrete should be on the steel.

Completed ☐

4. When the concrete arrives it should be spread in various parts of the form. It should not be placed in large quantities in one place and allowed to run or be worked over a long distance in the form. Segregation (separation) of the ingredients and sloping work planes result from this practice. Generally, concrete should be placed in horizontal layers having uniform thickness.

Completed ☐

Concrete should not be allowed to drop freely more than 3' or 4'. Drop chutes of rubber or metal may be used when placing concrete in thin vertical sections.

5. Placement of concrete in slab construction should be started at the most distant point of the work so that each batch may be dumped against the previously placed concrete, not away from it. Care should be taken to prevent stone pockets (areas of excessive large aggregate) from occurring.

Completed ☐

6. Work the mix with a spade or rod to be sure all spaces are filled and air pockets are worked out. This is called puddling, spading, or rodding. Mechanical vibrators can be used as well.

Completed ☐

Name_____

7. Be sure there is enough concrete in the form for the
   finishing operation. The next procedure is finishing.   Completed ☐

Proceed to Job 51.

Instructor's Initials:_____

Date: _____

Job Practice 50 Review ▬▬▬▬▬▬▬▬▬▬▬▬▬▬▬▬

After completing this job successfully, answer the following questions correctly:

1. What should govern the consistency of concrete?_____

_____

_____

2. What is the typical thickness of a sidewalk? _____

_____

3. What is the desired condition of the subgrade for the placement of concrete for a flat slab?_____

_____

_____

4. What personal safety equipment should be used when working with concrete?_____

_____

_____

5. What does segregation of concrete ingredients mean?_____

_____

6. What should you do immediately if you get cement in your eye? _____

_____

_____

Score: _____

Job Practice **51**
Finishing Concrete Slabs

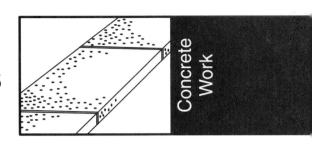

Concrete Work

Name_____

Date_____

Instructor_____

Period_____

This job practice continues Job 50.

Objective ▰▰▰▰▰▰▰▰▰▰▰▰▰▰▰▰▰▰▰▰▰▰▰▰▰▰▰▰▰▰▰▰

After completing this job you will be able to finish a concrete slab using proper technique.

Equipment ▰▰▰▰▰▰▰▰▰▰▰▰▰▰▰▰▰▰▰▰▰▰▰▰▰▰▰▰▰▰▰▰

To complete this job you will need the following tools and materials:

- ❖ Protective clothing
- ❖ Screed
- ❖ Darby or bullfloat
- ❖ Edgers
- ❖ Float
- ❖ Cement trowel
- ❖ Jointing tool
- ❖ Soft-bristled broom
- ❖ 1 × 10 board as wide as the slab

Recommended Procedure ▰▰▰▰▰▰▰▰▰▰▰▰▰▰▰▰▰▰▰

Study the appropriate section in Chapter 16 (Concrete Flatwork and Formed Shapes) before starting this job.

1. Screeding is usually the first finishing operation after the concrete is placed in the forms. Screeding is performed with a screed. See Illustration 51-1.

Illustration 51-1. Excess concrete is struck off with a screed.

Screeding is the process of striking off the excess concrete to bring the top surface to the proper grade or elevation. Rest the screed on the top of the form and move it across the concrete in a sawing motion. It is advanced forward slightly with each motion. This operation should be done before any bleeding (water rising to the surface) takes place. Screed the surface.   Completed ☐

2. The second operation is performed with a darby or bullfloat. This operation eliminates high and low spots and embeds large aggregate. See Illustration 51-2. This operation should follow immediately after screeding to prevent bleeding. Use the darby or bullfloat on the surface.   Completed ☐

Illustration 51-2. Bullfloat used to remove high and low spots.

Name_____

3. Edging is frequently the next operation. Edging provides a rounded edge or radius to prevent chipping or damage to the edge. The edger is run back and forth until the desired finish is obtained. See Illustration 51-3. Edge the slab.

Completed ❑

Illustration 51-3. Edging produces a radius on the edge of the slab.

4. Jointing is performed after edging. The cutting edge (bit) of the jointer cuts a groove in the slab to form a control or contraction joint. Cracking will occur at this point. Tooled joints are usually placed at intervals equal to the width of the slab, but not more than 20′ apart in sidewalks and driveways. Use a straightedge as a guide when making a groove. See Illustration 51-4. Joint the surface.

Completed ❑

Illustration 51-4. Jointing a slab.

5. After concrete has been edged and jointed, it should be allowed to harden enough to support a person and leave only a slight foot imprint. Floating should not begin until the water sheen has disappeared. The surface is floated with wood or metal floats or with a finishing machine using float blades. The light metal float forms a smoother surface texture than the wood float. Float the surface.

Completed ☐

6. When a smooth, dense surface is desired, steel troweling is performed after floating. Frequently a mason will float and trowel an area before moving their knee boards. As the concrete hardens, it may be troweled several times to obtain a very smooth and hard surface. See Illustration 51-5.

Illustration 51-5. Troweling a concrete slab.

If necessary, tooled joints and edges may be rerun after troweling to maintain uniformity. Some slabs are safer when broomed or brushed to produce a slightly roughened surface. This can be done with a soft-bristled push broom after the steel troweling. Brooming is usually perpendicular to the traffic direction.

Completed ☐

Instructor's Initials:_____

Date: _____

Job Practice 51 Review ▬▬▬▬▬▬▬▬▬▬▬▬▬

After completing this job successfully, answer the following questions correctly:

1. What is the purpose of screeding?_____

_____

_____

Name_____

2. What tool(s) is used to perform the second finishing operation on a concrete slab? _____
   _____

3. What is the purpose of edging a concrete slab? _____
   _____

4. Why is a concrete slab jointed? _____
   _____

5. When should floating begin? _____
   _____
   _____
   _____

6. What is the last operation in finishing a concrete slab when a smooth dense surface is desired?
   _____

Score: _____

Job Practice 52
Building Footing Forms for Concrete

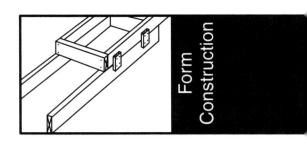

Name_____

Date_____

Instructor_____

Period _____

Objective

After completing this job you will be able to build footing forms for concrete using proper technique.

Equipment

To complete this job you will need the following tools and materials:

- ❖ Mason's or carpenter's hammer
- ❖ Saw
- ❖ Supply of 16 penny nails
- ❖ Seven 2″ × 4″ × 12″ stakes
- ❖ Three 2″ × 4″ × 8′ boards
- ❖ Level
- ❖ Framing square
- ❖ Flexible tape or folding rule
- ❖ Pencil
- ❖ Shovel
- ❖ Small sledgehammer

Recommended Procedure

Study the appropriate section in Chapter 15 (Form Construction) before starting this job.

Wood is the most popular form material. Both lumber and plywood are generally used in form construction. Forms must be strong enough to resist the forces developed by the plastic (liquid) concrete. Regular concrete weighs about 150 lb. per cu. ft. Safety is always a consideration in site-made forms.

Forms should be designed so that they are practical and economical and in the correct shape, width, and height. They must be able to retain their shape during the placing and curing phases. Wet concrete should not leak from joints and cause fins and ridges. They must also be designed so that they can be removed without damaging the concrete.

Footings are not usually visible and therefore appearance is of little concern. However, they must be located accurately and built to the specified dimensions. Concrete footing forms are usually constructed from 2″ construction lumber the same width as the footing thickness. The boards are placed on edge as shown in Illustration 52-1 and held in place by stakes and cross-spreaders.

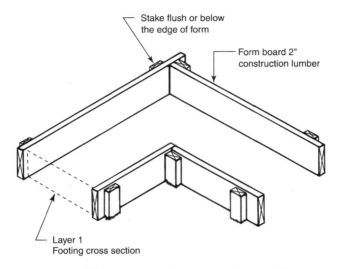

Illustration 52-1. Footing form made from 2″ construction lumber.

1. This job practice will require you to build an "L"-shape footing form that is 16″ wide. Each leg of the footing, which is measured along the outside of the "L" is 48″ long. The material is standard 2″ × 4″ construction lumber. Stakes are 2″ × 4″ pieces sharpened on the end. The stakes should be 12″ long. Prepare the materials.   Completed ❏

2. Using Illustration 52-1 as the pattern, cut your materials to length and prepare the stakes.   Completed ❏

3. Select the location for your footing form. Check with your instructor. Lay out the outside form boards and drive two stakes into the ground about 9″ deep. Place the outside form board against the stake and hold it with your foot while you drive a nail through the stake and then into the board enough to hold it in place. It should be slightly below the top edge of the form board.   Completed ❏

4. Go to the other stake, place the level on the form board and mark the point on the stake where the form board is level. Remove the level and nail the stake to the form board. Use two nails. Go to the first stake and complete the process there. Use the shovel to level the ground some if there is a high spot.   Completed ❏

5. Check the board to see if it is still level. If not, drive the stake down some at the high end.   Completed ❏

6. Proceed to build the rest of the form using this approach. Regularly check to see that the form is level and the proper width and length.   Completed ❏

Name_____

7. When all the boards are in place, check all dimensions and
be sure the form is level across as well as along the form.   Completed ❑

8. When you are satisfied it is correct, ask your instructor to
inspect it.   Completed ❑

9. Take the form apart, remove all nails, and return all tools
and materials to their proper places.   Completed ❑

Instructor's Initials:_____

Date: _____

Job Practice 52 Review ▪▬▬▬▬▬▬▬▬▬▬▬▬

After completing this job successfully, answer the following questions correctly:

1. How much does regular concrete weigh? _____

   _____

2. In addition to retaining their shape and not leaking, what is another major consideration in the design
   and construction of concrete forms? _____

   _____

3. What is the most popular material used to make site-made concrete forms?_____

   _____

4. How can curved shapes be formed using wood forms? _____

   _____

   _____

   _____

5. Why should the stakes *not* project above the top edge of concrete slab forms?_____

   _____

Score: _____

Job Practice 53
Building Wall Forms for Concrete

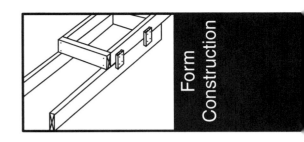

Name_____

Date_____

Instructor _____

Period _____

Objective

After completing this job you will be able to build a wall form for concrete using proper technique.

Equipment

To complete this job you will need the following tools and materials:

- ❖ Mason's or carpenter's hammer
- ❖ Supply of 6 and 16 penny nails
- ❖ Flexible tape or folding rule
- ❖ Supply of 2″ × 4″ lumber
- ❖ Supply of 3/4″ exterior plywood
- ❖ Four crimp snap-in form ties
- ❖ Concrete nails or power driven nails
- ❖ Saw
- ❖ Level
- ❖ Framing square
- ❖ Pencil
- ❖ Power drill
- ❖ Safety equipment

Recommended Procedure

Study the appropriate section of Chapter 15 (Form Construction) before starting this job.

This job involves building a wall form 32″ high by 48″ long for a concrete wall 10″ thick. The wall form should be anchored to a footing (or floor) as shown in Illustration 53-1.

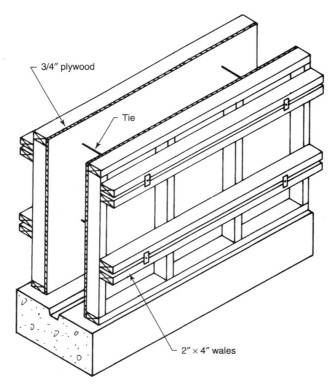

Illustration 53-1. Typical site-made wall form.

1. To build an in-place wall form, first cut two sole plates, two top plates, and eight studs. The plates should be 48″ long and the studs 29″. (A 2″ × 4″ stud is actually 1 1/2″ × 3 1/2″.)

    Completed ❑

2. Lay out the pieces and nail them together with 16 penny common nails. Use two nails per connection. Be sure the studs are spaced 16″ apart and the frame is square. Build two identical frames.

    Completed ❑

3. Cut two pieces of sheathing to fit the frames (32″ × 48″). Nail the sheathing to the frames using 6 penny box nails.

    Completed ❑

4. Mark the location on the footing where the forms will be located to produce a 10″ thick concrete wall. The form should be centered on the footing.

    Completed ❑

5. Ask someone to help you lift each frame to its location on the footing. Attach each frame to the footing using concrete nails or power driven nails. Do not use a power activated nailer until you have instruction in its proper use. Be sure to wear safety glasses, hard hat, etc.

    Completed ❑

6. Determine the four locations of the form ties. See Illustration 53-1 again. Drill a hole at each location large enough to receive the tie. Repeat the operation on the other form.

    Completed ❑

7. Insert the form ties through the holes as per the manufacturer's instructions.

    Completed ❑

Name_____

8. Cut eight 2″ × 4″ × 48″ wales. Ask someone to help you hold
a pair of wales in place while you tighten the snap-tie. Wales
are not nailed to the form. Complete the process by
attaching all of the ties to the wales.   Completed ❑

9. Check the assembly for proper spacing and then be sure it
is level and plumb. Make any adjustments necessary.   Completed ❑

10. Clean up the work area and return all tools and materials to
their assigned places.   Completed ❑

Save this assembly for Job 54.

Instructor's Initials:_____

Date: _____

Job Practice 53 Review

After completing this job successfully, answer the following questions correctly:

1. Name the five basic structural parts of a wall form. _____

_____

2. How is the proper spacing maintained between the two sides of a typical site-constructed wall form?

_____

_____

3. How are the wales attached to the wall forms? _____

_____

4. What methods are generally used to attach the sole plate to the footing? _____

_____

5. What kind of plywood is used for sheathing in a wood wall form?_____

_____

_____

Score: _____

Job Practice **54**
Building and Installing a Buck

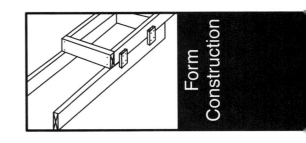

Form Construction

Name_____

Date_____

Instructor _____

Period _____

Objective

After completing this job you will be able to build and install a buck in a wall form using proper technique.

Equipment

To complete this job you will need the following tools and materials:

- ❖ Mason's or carpenter's hammer
- ❖ Saw
- ❖ Supply of 6 penny nails
- ❖ Level
- ❖ Framing square
- ❖ Flexible tape or folding rule
- ❖ Pencil
- ❖ Supply of 1″ × 12″ pine boards or 3/4″ plywood
- ❖ Safety equipment

Recommended Procedure

Study the appropriate section of Chapter 15 (Form Construction) before starting this job. This job involves building a 12″ × 18″ buck to be placed in the wall form constructed in Job Practice 53.

Any openings in the wall, such as windows, can be formed using bucks. Bucks are wood or steel frames set in the form between the inner and outer form to make an opening in the wall. See Illustration 54-1.

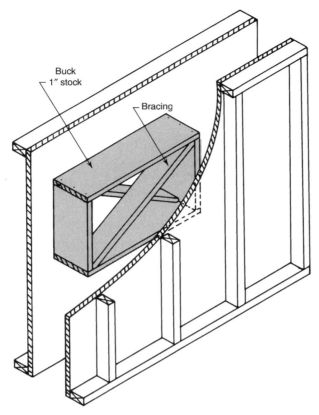

Illustration 54-1. A buck in a typical wall form.

1. To build a buck for placement in a wall form, first lay out the lengths needed and check your dimensions before cutting the pieces. The buck will be 12″ high by 18″ wide (outside dimensions). Don't forget to subtract the material thickness for the end pieces.   Completed ❑

2. Cut the four sides of the buck to proper length and width. Check the distance between the forms to be sure your buck will fit snugly between them.   Completed ❑

3. Nail the frame together, being sure that the corners are perpendicular (90°). Check the assembly with the framing square.   Completed ❑

4. Measure the inside diagonal distance from corner-to-corner and cut two 6″ wide boards to serve as braces. Study the illustration again. Cut the pieces when you are sure the dimensions are correct.   Completed ❑

5. Nail the braces in place. Be careful not to rack the buck during this operation.   Completed ❑

Name_____

6. Place the buck in the wall form and secure it with four nails on each side of the buck. Do not drive these nails all the way so they can be pulled before removing the wall forms. (Special form nails are made for this purpose.) Be sure the buck is level in the form. Locate the nails by measuring from the end and top of the form.   Completed ❑

7. Inspect your work, clean up the area, and return all tools and materials to their assigned places.   Completed ❑

Instructor's Initials:_____

Date: _____

Job Practice 54 Review ▬▬▬▬▬▬▬▬▬▬▬▬▬▬▬▬▬

After completing this job successfully, answer the following questions correctly:

1. What is the purpose of a buck? _____

_____

_____

2. What technique is used in wood buck construction to prevent racking? _____

_____

3. How can you recognize a form nail? _____

_____

4. Based on the experience gained from this job practice, when would be the best time to install the buck between the forms? _____

_____

_____

5. When building a buck, what dimensions are most critical? _____

_____

_____

Score: _____

Job Practice 55
Installing Round Column Forms

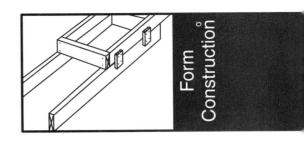

Name_____

Date_____

Instructor _____

Period _____

Objective

After completing this job you will be able to install a round column form using proper technique.

Equipment

To complete this job you will need the following tools and materials:

- ❖ Mason's or carpenter's hammer
- ❖ Saw
- ❖ Supply of 16 penny nails
- ❖ Level
- ❖ Flexible tape or folding rule
- ❖ Pencil
- ❖ Supply of 2″ × 4″ material
- ❖ Safety equipment
- ❖ A round paper column form

Recommended Procedure

Study the appropriate section in Chapter 15 (Form Construction) before starting this job.

Concrete columns reinforced with steel are commonly cast in square, rectangular, and round shapes. Forms for the square and rectangular columns are easily constructed from wood. However, round column forms are usually metal, fiberboard, or paper. See Illustration 55-1. Round prefabricated forms are produced for various lengths and diameters. Forms made from fiberboard and paper are not reusable, but have some advantages. They are economical, lightweight, and the paper surfaces produce a very smooth concrete surface with no seams.

Illustration 55-1. A paper column form.

This job involves the installation of a paper form to produce a round concrete column.

1. Identify the location where the column form is to be positioned. The surface should be a footing or over a hole in the ground.   Completed ☐

2. Examine the column form to be sure it is not damaged and is the proper diameter and length for the job. If the form is too long, it can be cut with a hand or power saw.   Completed ☐

3. Using 2 × 4 lumber, build a scaffold type support system around the column form. This should be a sturdy structure as it will serve as the bracing for the column. Remember it will weigh several hundred pounds when filled with concrete. Do not nail into the form itself.   Completed ☐

4. Adjust the form until it is perfectly vertical and nail boards across the framework to prevent the form from moving.   Completed ☐

Name_____

5. Be sure that concrete will not leak out around the bottom of
    the form. It should be snug against the footing or down in the
    hole if placed over a hole.   Completed ❑

6. Look over the total assembly to be sure it is safe and well
    constructed. When you are satisfied it is correct, clean up
    the area and return all tools and materials to their assigned
    places.   Completed ❑

                                    Instructor's Initials:_____

                                    Date: _____

Job Practice 55 Review

After completing this job successfully, answer the following questions correctly:

1. What materials are frequently used for round concrete column forms? _____

    _____

2. What type of round concrete column forms are reusable? _____

    _____

3. Identify three advantages of forms made from fiberboard and paper. _____

    _____

    _____

    _____

4. What type of material is generally used to brace a paper concrete column form? _____

    _____

5. How can paper forms be cut to length? _____

    _____

                                                      Score:_____

Job Practice 56
Building Centering for a Masonry Arch

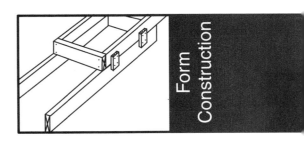

Name_____

Date_____

Instructor _____

Period _____

Objective

After completing this job you will be able to build centering for a masonry arch using proper technique.

Equipment

To complete this job you will need the following tools and materials:

❖ Mason's or carpenter's hammer

❖ Saws

❖ Flexible tape or folding rule

❖ Pencil

❖ Supply of 1″ × 2″ pine boards

❖ Two 2″ × 8″ × 4′ boards

❖ Supply of 8 penny box nails

❖ Cardboard arch pattern

❖ Square

❖ Mason's cord

Recommended Procedure

Study the appropriate section in Chapter 15 (Form Construction) and Chapter 13 (Construction Details) before starting this job.

Arch centering is designed to support the masonry while it is being constructed. Arch centering is usually made from wood. The ribs are 2″ construction lumber and the lagging may be 1″ × 2″ pine strips. The lagging should be cut 1″ shorter than the thickness of the masonry wall so it will not interfere with the mason's line. The ribs are cut to the shape of the arch. The centering must be sturdy to support the weight of the masonry units. See Illustration 56-1.

This job will involve the construction of the centering for a segmental arch in an 8″ thick brick masonry wall. The width of the arch is 36″.

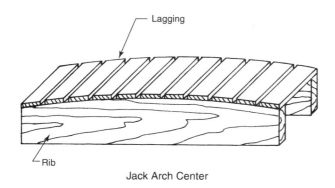

Jack Arch Center

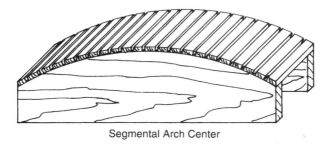

Segmental Arch Center

Illustration 56-1. Centering for an arch.

1. If a cardboard pattern of the arch is available, examine it to be sure it is the proper design and size. If a pattern is not available, then make one. The total width should be 36″ and the rise may be 1/6, 1/8, 1/10, or 1/12 of the span. We will use 1/12 for this job. Therefore, the rise will be 3″. See Illustration 56-2. Make a pattern using mason's cord and a pencil.

Completed ❑

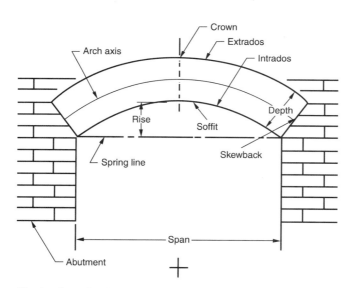

Illustration 56-2. Arch terminology.

Name_____

2. Using your pattern, lay out the arch intrados (lower curve of the arch) on one of the 2″ × 8″ rib boards after they have been cut to a length of 36″. Position the pattern such that the top of the curve is almost to the edge of the board. Mark out the curve on the rib board.   Completed ❏

3. Saw out the curve using a jigsaw or band saw. Be sure you are familiar with these tools before using them.   Completed ❏

4. Using the same process, lay out the curve on the other rib board. These two boards must be identical. Cut out this curve.   Completed ❏

5. Using the 1″ × 2″ material, cut several strips 7″ long to form the lagging. Note two of them should be beveled on the edge to continue the vertical end of the centering.   Completed ❏

6. Nail several lagging strips into place leaving 1/2″ to 3/4″ between them. Cut the remaining strips and nail them to the rib boards.   Completed ❏

7. Check over your work, clean up the area, and return all tools and materials to their assigned places.   Completed ❏

Instructor's Initials:_____

Date: _____

Job Practice 56 Review ▬▬▬▬▬▬▬▬▬▬▬▬

After completing this job successfully, answer the following questions correctly:

1. What is the purpose of arch centering? _____

_____

2. What is lagging?_____

_____

3. How is the shape of the ribs determined? _____

_____

4. What would the rise of a segmental arch be if it were 48″ wide and had a rise of 1/8 the span?____

_____

5. Why was a jigsaw or band saw recommended to cut the curve on the centering ribs? _____

_____

6. Why are narrow strips used for lagging? _____

_____

Score: _____

Job Practice 57
Dampproofing Concrete Block Basement Walls

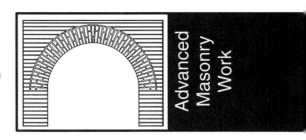

Advanced Masonry Work

Name_____

Date_____

Instructor _____

Period _____

Objective

After completing this job you will be able to dampproof a concrete block basement wall using proper technique.

Equipment

To complete this job you will need the following tools and materials:

- ❖ Plasterer's trowel
- ❖ Supply of Portland cement plaster or mortar
- ❖ Wire scratcher
- ❖ Bituminous dampproofing compound or cement-based paint
- ❖ Mason's trowel
- ❖ Stiff bristle brush
- ❖ Hard hat, safety glasses, etc.

Recommended Procedure

Study the appropriate section in Chapter 13 (Construction Details) before starting this job.

1. Apply a 1/4″ thick parge coat of Portland cement plaster or mortar to the outside of a clean and damp concrete block basement wall. Use the plasterer's rectangular trowel for this operation. The coat should be worked into the cracks and crevices to form a watertight barrier. See Illustration 57-1.

Completed ❑

Illustration 57-1. Applying the first parge coat to a basement wall.

2. Allow the first parge coat to partially harden and then roughen it with a scratcher to provide a good bond for the second coat. See Illustration 57-2. Keep the first coat moist for 24 hours.

Completed ☐

Illustration 57-2. Using the wire scratcher to roughen the first parge coat.

Name_____

3. After 24 hours, the first parge coat should be sufficiently cured to apply the second coat. Apply another 1/4″ thick parge coat to the wall. Apply firm pressure and leave the surface smooth and dense. See Illustration 57-3.

Completed ❑

Illustration 57-3. Applying the second parge coat.

4. Form a cove over the footing to prevent water from collecting at this point. The second coat should be allowed to cure for at least 48 hours before applying any further dampproofing.

Completed ❑

5. For added moisture resistance, apply a heavy coat of tar, two coats of a cement-based paint, or a covering of plastic film to the wall. Follow manufacturer's instructions when using any proprietary product.

Completed ❑

Instructor's Initials:_____

Date: _____

Job Practice 57 Review

After completing this job successfully, answer the following questions correctly:

1. What material is commonly used as a parge coat to dampproof a concrete block basement wall?

_____

2. How many coats of parging are recommended to dampproof a concrete block basement wall?

_____

3. What tool is recommended to apply a parge coat? _____

   _____

4. Why is a scratcher used on the first parge coat?_____

   _____

   _____

5. What is the function of the cove between the wall and the footing? _____

   _____

   _____

6. What type of materials may be used over a parged wall to increase resistance to moisture penetration?

   _____

   _____

   _____

                                                            Score: _____

Job Practice **58**
Building Columns, Piers, and Pilasters

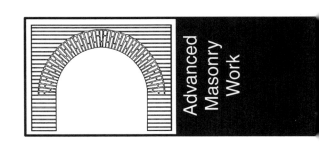

Advanced Masonry Work

Name_____

Date_____

Instructor_____

Period_____

Objective

After completing this job you will be able to build brick and block columns, piers, and pilasters using proper technique.

Equipment

To complete this job you will need the following tools and materials:

- ❖ Mason's tools
- ❖ Mortar
- ❖ Supply of bricks and blocks
- ❖ Hard hat, safety glasses, etc.

Recommended Procedure

Study the appropriate section in Chapter 13 (Construction Details) before starting this job.

Columns, piers, and pilasters transmit loads to the footing. Columns and piers are freestanding, but pilasters are built into the foundation wall.

This job will provide an opportunity to build a column, a pier, and a pilaster using brick and block.

Constructing a 12″ × 12″ brick column

1. Assemble the materials to build a 12″ × 12″ brick column on a footing to a height of 12 courses. (A column's height is at least three times its thickness, by definition.) See Illustration 58-1.

Completed ☐

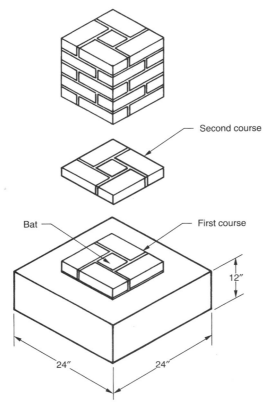

Illustration 58-1. Bonding for a 12″ × 12″ brick column.

2. Lay the first course of bricks on the footing in the designated location. Use full bed joints and check to see that this course is level, plumb, and square.

Completed ☐

3. Using the bond pattern illustrated for the second course, lay the second course. Remove excess mortar and level this course.

Completed ☐

4. Complete the column to 12 courses. The structure should be a solid mass of bricks and mortar that is square, plumb, and level. Tool the joints and brush the bricks.

Completed ☐

Constructing a 16″ × 16″ concrete block pier

1. Assemble the materials needed to construct a 16″ × 16″ concrete block pier to a height of three courses.

Completed ☐

2. Mark the location for the pier. Lay down a solid mortar bed and place the first course. See Illustration 58-2.

Completed ☐

Name_____

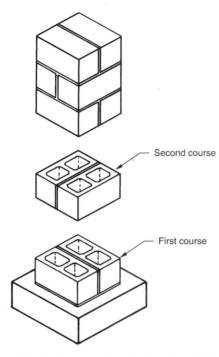

Illustration 58-2. Concrete block pier, 16″ × 16″ square.

3. Lay the second and third courses alternating the position of the blocks as shown in the illustration. The third course should be solid top blocks.

Completed ☐

4. Tool the joints and brush the blocks.

Completed ☐

Constructing a 4″ × 12″ brick and block pilaster

1. Assemble the materials needed to build an 8″ × 44″ long concrete block wall that incorporates a 4″ × 12″ brick pilaster. Wall height will be 32″ high. See Illustration 58-3.

Completed ☐

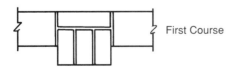
First Course

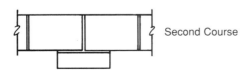
Second Course

4″ × 12″ Projection

Illustration 58-3. Brick pilaster in concrete block wall.

2. Snap a line to fix the location of the wall. Lay down a full bed of mortar and lay a regular 8″ × 8″ × 16″ concrete block at either end of the wall. The remaining space should accommodate a 12″ long brick.   Completed ❑

3. Fill in the first course of bricks for the pilaster as shown in the illustration. Check the first course of blocks and bricks to be sure they are level, plumb, and straight.   Completed ❑

4. Lay two more courses of bricks to bring the pilaster up to the height of the course of blocks. Alternate the course pattern.   Completed ❑

5. Lay the next course of blocks and fill in the bricks as you proceed. Study the illustration of the second course. You will need to cut some blocks to make the pattern come out right.   Completed ❑

6. Lay the third course of blocks and bricks the same as the first course. Tool the joints and brush the wall.   Completed ❑

7. Clean up the area and return the tools and materials to their assigned places.   Completed ❑

Instructor's Initials:_____

Date: _____

Job Practice 58 Review

After completing this job successfully, answer the following questions correctly:

1. What is the function of columns, piers, and pilasters?_____
   _____
   _____

2. Which is generally taller, a column or a pier? _____
   _____

3. Why were solid top blocks used as the final course on the concrete block pier that you constructed?
   _____
   _____

4. Why were bricks used to build the 4″ × 12″ pilaster in the concrete block wall?_____
   _____
   _____
   _____

5. What type of bonding was used in the pilaster to gain its strength? _____
   _____
   _____

Score: _____

Job Practice 59
Building Solid Masonry Walls

Name_____

Date_____

Instructor_____

Period _____

Objective

After completing this job you will be able to build solid masonry walls of brick and block using proper technique.

Equipment

To accomplish this job you will need the following tools and materials:

- ❖ Mason's tools
- ❖ Mortar
- ❖ Supply of bricks and blocks
- ❖ Hard hat, safety glasses, etc.

Recommended Procedure

Study the appropriate section in Chapter 13 (Construction Details) before starting this job.

There are six generally accepted types of masonry walls: solid walls, 4″ RBM curtain and panel walls, hollow walls, anchored veneer walls, composite walls, and reinforced walls. Job practice 59 deals with solid masonry walls.

A solid masonry wall is built up of masonry units laid close together with all joints between them filled with mortar. Solid or hollow masonry units or a combination of these materials may be used.

This job practice will provide an opportunity to construct two types of solid masonry walls, one using solid units (brick) and one using hollow units (block).

Solid brick masonry wall with headers

1. Assemble the materials necessary to build the solid brick masonry demonstration wall shown in Illustration 59-1.

Completed ☐

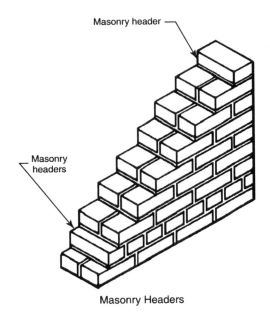

Masonry header

Masonry headers

Masonry Headers

Illustration 59-1. A solid brick masonry wall with masonry headers.

2. Lay both wythes of the first course of bricks in running bond. Use full mortar bed and fill the collar joint between the wythes.

Completed ☐

3. Lay the second course as headers. See the illustration.

Completed ☐

4. Lay the next six courses in running bond identical to the first course. Keep your work neat and clean.

Completed ☐

5. Lay the final course as headers similar to the second course. Tool the joints and brush the wall.

Completed ☐

Solid masonry wall using hollow units masonry bonded

1. Assemble the materials needed to build the 12″ thick demonstration wall shown in Illustration 59-2.

Completed ☐

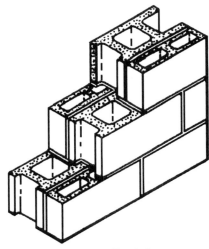

Masonry Bonded

Illustration 59-2. A solid masonry wall using hollow concrete block.

Name_____

2. Lay both wythes of blocks (4″ and 8″ blocks) in running bond on a solid mortar bed. Fill the collar joint between the wythes.   Completed ❑

3. Lay the back wythe of the second course. Parge the face to form the collar joint between the wythes. Be sure to alternate the 4″ and 8″ blocks to develop the masonry bond.   Completed ❑

4. Lay the front wythe and add more mortar to the collar joint if needed.   Completed ❑

5. Complete the demonstration wall by laying the third course identical to the first. Tool the joints and brush the wall.   Completed ❑

6. Inspect your work, clean up the area, and return all tools and materials to their assigned places.   Completed ❑

Instructor's Initials:_____

Date: _____

Job Practice 59 Review ▰▰▰▰▰▰▰▰▰▰▰▰▰▰▰▰▰

After completing this job successfully, answer the following questions correctly:

1. What are the six types of masonry walls generally recognized? _____

_____

_____

_____

_____

2. Is it permissible to use hollow masonry units to build a solid masonry wall? Why? _____

_____

_____

3. What is the function of the collar joint in a solid masonry wall?_____

_____

_____

4. What size concrete block units are used to build a 12″ thick solid masonry wall? _____

_____

5. Which wythe was laid first in the 12″ thick solid masonry wall?_____

_____

Score: _____

Job Practice 60
Building a 4" RBM Curtain or Panel Wall

Advanced Masonry Work

Name_____

Date_____

Instructor _____

Period _____

Objective

After completing this job you will be able to build a 4" RBM (reinforced brick masonry) panel or curtain wall using proper technique.

Equipment

To accomplish this job you will need the following tools and materials:

❖ Mason's tools

❖ Mortar

❖ Supply of bricks

❖ Steel reinforcing

❖ Red hat, safety glasses, etc.

❖ Flashing and wicking

Recommended Procedure

Study the appropriate section of Chapter 13 (Construction Details) before starting this job.

A curtain wall is an exterior nonloadbearing wall not wholly supported at each story. A panel wall is an exterior nonloadbearing wall supported at each story. Both walls must be able to resist lateral forces such as wind pressures and transfer these forces to adjacent structural members. Illustration 60-1 shows a typical 4" RBM wall.

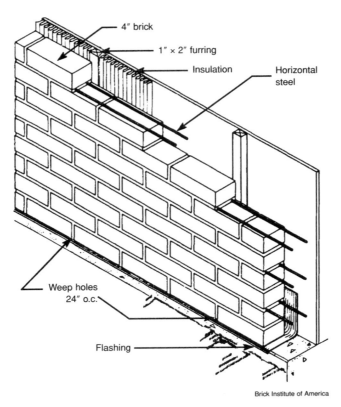

Illustration 60-1. Typical 4″ RBM curtain or panel wall. (BIA)

Ladder or truss-type joint reinforcement is used throughout the length of the wall. Reinforcement must be completely embedded in mortar, not laid directly on top of the brick. All head and bed joints must be full to resist wind driven rain.

1. Assemble the materials needed for this job. Assume the demonstration wall will be 6′ long, 4″ thick, and 9 courses high. Lay the bricks to the number six on the modular rule.

Completed ☐

2. Position the flashing along a chalk line or edge of a slab or foundation brick ledge. Lay down a full mortar bed for the first course, but allow for weep holes every 24″ along the wall. Lay the first course of stretchers.

Completed ☐

3. Lay the second course in running bond on a full bed of mortar. Position the joint reinforcement (ladder or truss-type) on small pads of mortar so that it will be in the center of the mortar joint.

Completed ☐

4. Lay the third course of bricks on a full bed of mortar being careful not to disturb the reinforcement.

Completed ☐

5. Repeat the process inserting reinforcing in every other bed joint. See the illustration. Continue until the wall is 9 courses high.

Completed ☐

Name_____

6. Tool the joints and brush the wall. Examine your work to be
   sure it is high quality.   Completed ☐

7. Clean up the area and return the tools and materials to their
   assigned places.   Completed ☐

Instructor's Initials:_____

Date: _____

Job Practice 60 Review ▰▰▰▰▰▰▰▰▰▰▰▰▰▰▰▰

After completing this job successfully, answer the following questions correctly:

1. What does *RBM* represent? _____

   _____

2. What is the difference between a curtain wall and a panel wall? _____

   _____

   _____

   _____

   _____

3. Why is reinforcing required in single wythe curtain and panel walls? _____

   _____

   _____

4. What type of reinforcing was used in your RBM wall? _____

   _____

   _____

5. Is it possible to lay a single wythe brick wall in common bond? _____

   _____

   _____

6. What will determine how frequently joint reinforcing should be placed in an RBM wall? _____

   _____

   _____

Score: _____

Job Practice 61
Building Hollow Masonry Bonded Walls

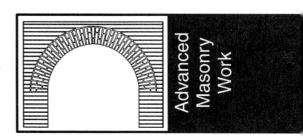

Advanced Masonry Work

Name_____

Date_____

Instructor _____

Period _____

Objective

After completing this job you will be able to build hollow masonry bonded walls of brick and block using proper technique.

Equipment

To accomplish this job you will need the following tools and materials:

❖ Mason's tools

❖ Mortar

❖ Supply of bricks and blocks

❖ Hard hat, safety glasses, etc.

Recommended Procedure

Study the appropriate section of Chapter 13 (Construction Details) before starting this job.

Hollow walls are the third type of masonry walls. They are built using solid or hollow masonry units. The units are separated to form an inner and an outer wall. They may be either a cavity or masonry bonded type wall. Cavity walls were covered in Job Practices 28 and 35. This job practice will deal with masonry bonded type walls. You will have an opportunity to construct a hollow masonry wall using solid units (brick).

Hollow brick masonry bonded wall

This demonstration wall will be 8″ thick and will use the pattern shown in Illustration 61-1. Notice the stretcher courses are laid as rowlock stretchers while the alternate courses are laid as rowlock headers.

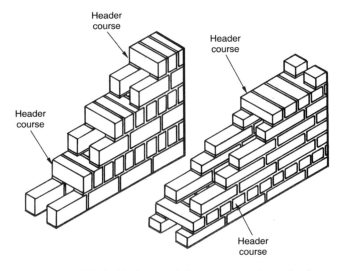

Illustration 61-1. Hollow brick masonry bonded wall.

1. Assemble the materials needed for this job. This wall will be 8″ thick, 32″ long, and 6 courses high.   Completed ☐

2. Snap two chalk lines where the two sides of the wall will be located. Lay a bed of mortar for the inside wythe.   Completed ☐

3. Lay the inner wythe of brick as rowlock stretchers. Remove excess mortar between the wythes. Lay the outer wythe to the line. Check the distance between the faces of the wall to be sure it equals the length of a brick.   Completed ☐

4. Lay the second course as rowlock headers. Use full head joints.   Completed ☐

5. Repeat the pattern until the wall is 6 courses high.   Completed ☐

6. Strike the joints and brush the wall.   Completed ☐

7. Inspect your work, clean up the area, and return all tools and materials to their assigned places.   Completed ☐

Instructor's Initials:_____

Date: _____

Job Practice 61 Review

After completing this job successfully, answer the following questions correctly:

1. What wall type is similar to the hollow masonry bonded wall? _____

Name_____

2. What is the basic difference between the hollow masonry bonded wall and the cavity wall? _____

_____

_____

_____

_____

3. Which wythe was laid first on the hollow masonry bonded wall?_____

_____

4. How was the width of the wall determined? _____

_____

5. Rowlock stretchers were used to provide the cavity space in this wall. Could regular headers have been used? Why?_____

_____

_____

_____

Score: _____

Job Practice 62

Building an Anchored Veneered Wall and Installing Flashing

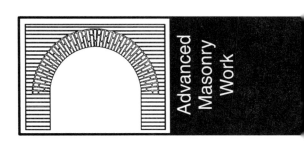

Advanced Masonry Work

Objective

After completing this job you will be able to build an anchored veneered wall and install flashing using proper technique.

Equipment

To accomplish this job you will need the following tools and materials:

- ❖ Mason's tools
- ❖ Mortar
- ❖ Supply of bricks
- ❖ Supply of corrugated fasteners
- ❖ Hard hat, safety glasses, etc.
- ❖ Section of frame wall

Recommended Procedure

Study the appropriate section of Chapter 13 (Construction Details) before starting this job.

Brick and stone masonry units are widely used as a facing veneer. In this application, loadbearing properties of the materials are not used. The veneer is attached to the backing, but does not act structurally with the rest of the wall.

Anchored brick veneer construction consists of a nominal 3" or 4" thick exterior brick wythe anchored to the backing system (frequently a frame wall) with metal ties in such a way that a clear air space is provided between the veneer and the backing system. The backing system may be wood frame, steel frame, concrete, or masonry.

Brick or stone veneer on a frame backing must transfer the weight of the veneer to the foundation. The foundation brick ledge should be at least equal to the total thickness of the brick veneer wall assembly.

There should be a tie for every 2 2/3 sq. ft. of wall area with a maximum spacing of 24″ o.c. in either direction. The best location of the nail is at the bend (not greater than 5/8″ away from the bend) in the corrugated tie, and the bend should be 90°. Corrugated ties must also penetrate to at least half the veneer thickness and completely embedded in the mortar.

This job provides the opportunity to build a section of brick or stone veneered wall with a typical frame wall backup. The length of the section is 48″ and the height is 9 courses.

1. Assemble the tools and materials needed for the job. Arrange a convenient work area. See Illustration 62-1.　　　　　　　　　　　**Completed ❑**

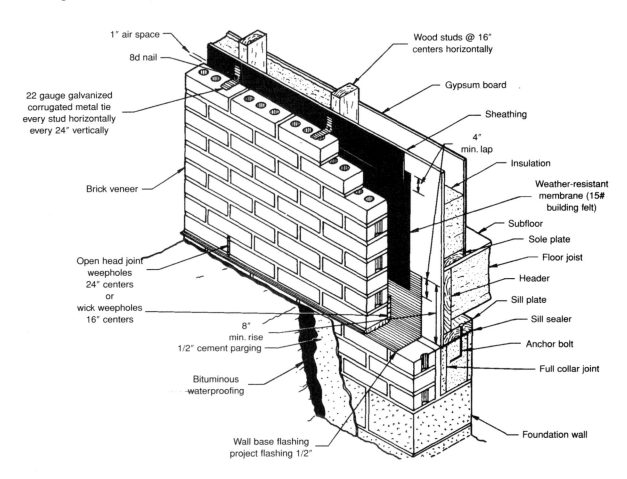

Illustration 62-1. Typical brick veneer wall with wood frame backup.

2. Snap a chalk line to locate the face of the veneer if the demonstration wall is on the floor. Place the flashing in its proper location and lay a full bed of mortar.　　　　　　　**Completed ❑**

3. Lay the first course of brick or stone maintaining a 1″ air space between the veneer and the backup. Install two weep holes about 24″ apart by omitting the head joints.　　　　　　**Completed ❑**

4. Straightedge and level the course. Lay the second course of masonry units on a full mortar bed. Be sure the weep holes remain open.　　　　　　　　　　　　　　　　　**Completed ❑**

Name_____

5. Attach a corrugated fastener (tie) to each stud so that it will fit into the mortar joint between the second and third courses of masonry. Bend them into place. See Illustration 62-2.

Completed ☐

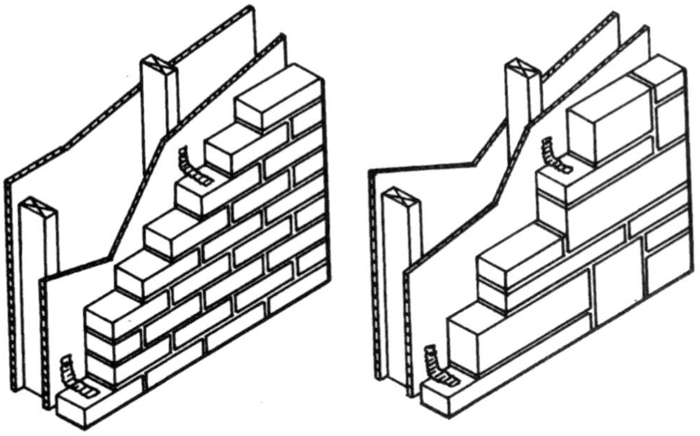

Brick Veneer on Frame   Stone Veneer on Frame

Illustration 62-2. Brick and stone veneer attached to frame construction.

6. String a bed of mortar for the third course being sure to put mortar above and below the metal ties. Lay the third course.

Completed ☐

7. Continue laying courses until you reach the eighth course. Attach metal ties between the eighth and ninth courses.

Completed ☐

8. Lay the ninth and final course. Strike the joints and brush the wall.

Completed ☐

9. Inspect your work, clean up the area, and return tools and materials to their assigned places.

Completed ☐

Instructor's Initials:_____

Date: _____

Job Practice 62 Review ▬▬▬▬▬▬▬▬▬▬▬

After completing this job successfully, answer the following questions correctly:

1. Why would brick, stone, or concrete masonry units be used as a facing in an anchored veneered wall since they are generally used in loadbearing applications? _____

_____

_____

2. How are the masonry units bonded to the backup wall in anchored veneered walls? _____

_____

3. Why is an air space of 1″ generally used in an anchored veneered wall?_____

_____

_____

4. How is the moisture that collects in the air space removed?_____

_____

_____

5. What kind of material is generally used as flashing in an anchored veneered wall?_____

_____

_____

_____

_____

Score: _____

Job Practice 63
Building a 12" Composite Brick and Block Wall

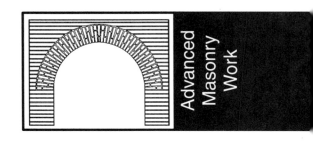

Advanced Masonry Work

Name_____

Date_____

Instructor _____

Period _____

Objective

After you have completed this job you will be able to build a 12" composite brick and block wall using proper technique.

Equipment

To accomplish this job you will need the following tools and materials:

- ❖ Mason's tools
- ❖ Mortar
- ❖ Supply of bricks and blocks
- ❖ Supply of header blocks
- ❖ Hard hat, safety glasses, etc.

Recommended Procedure

Study the appropriate section of Chapter 13 (Construction Details) before you start this job.

A 12" composite wall is constructed in a manner similar to the 8" composite wall, but a header block is used in the 12" wall. The header block may be laid with the recessed notch up or down, depending on construction requirements. In Illustration 63-1 header blocks were used for the sixth course bonding.

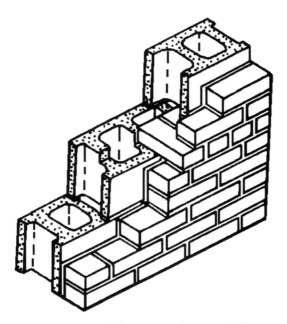

Illustration 63-1. A 12″ composite wall with a masonry bond used to tie the wythes together.

The demonstration wall to be built will be 12″ thick, 24″ high, and 48″ long. Header block will be used to provide sixth course bonding.

1. Assemble the tools and materials needed for this job and prepare a work area.   Completed ❑

2. Snap a chalk line to fix the location of the wall. Lay down a mortar bed for the course of concrete block. Lay three stretcher blocks as the back wythe.   Completed ❑

3. Lay three courses of bricks as the front wythe. Fill the collar joints and use full head joints. Be sure the bricks and blocks are the same height at this point.   Completed ❑

4. Lay the second course of blocks on the back wythe. These are header blocks with the notch facing up.   Completed ❑

5. Lay two courses of bricks on the front wythe in running bond. Then lay the next course as headers to tie the wythes together. Level, plumb, and straightedge the assembly.   Completed ❑

6. Lay the third course of concrete blocks on the back wythe. Then, lay bricks up to the height of the blocks (9 courses).   Completed ❑

7. Tool the joints and brush the wall. Inspect your work.   Completed ❑

8. Clean up the area and return the tools and materials to their assigned places.   Completed ❑

Instructor's Initials:_____

Date: _____

Name_____

Job Practice 63 Review ▬▬▬▬▬▬▬▬▬▬▬▬▬▬▬▬

After completing this job successfully, answer the following questions correctly:

1. What is the basic difference in construction between an 8″ composite and a 12″ composite wall?

_____

_____

2. Why are no metal ties required in the 12″ composite wall? _____

_____

_____

3. Which wythe was begun first in this wall? _____

_____

4. How many courses of bricks equaled one course of blocks in this job? _____

_____

5. What is the name of the bond on the front wythe (brick)? _____

_____

Score: _____

Job Practice **64**
Building Reinforced Masonry Walls

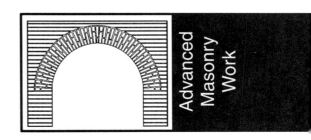

Advanced Masonry Work

Name_____

Date_____

Instructor _____

Period _____

Objective

After you have completed this job you will be able to build a reinforced concrete block wall and a reinforced brick masonry wall using proper technique.

Equipment

To accomplish this job you will need the following tools and materials:

- ❖ Mason's tools
- ❖ Mortar
- ❖ Supply of bricks
- ❖ Supply of two cell blocks and lintel blocks
- ❖ Two steel bars 3/8″ × 32″
- ❖ Four steel bars 1/2″ × 32″
- ❖ Hard hat, safety glasses, etc.

Recommended Procedure

Study the appropriate section of Chapter 13 (Construction Details) before you start this job.

Reinforced walls are built with steel reinforcement embedded with the masonry units. The walls are structurally bonded by grout which is poured into the cavity (collar joint) between the wythes of masonry when solid units are used. Grout is poured in the cells of hollow units when concrete blocks are used.

Reinforced masonry walls should be reinforced with an area of steel not less than 0.002 times the cross-sectional area of the wall. Not more than 2/3 of this area may be used in either direction. Maximum spacing of principal reinforcement should not exceed 48″.

This job will provide the opportunity to build two reinforced masonry walls—one with hollow units (concrete block) and one with solid units (brick). Each demonstration wall is to be 32″ long and 24″ high.

Reinforced masonry wall using hollow units (concrete blocks)

Illustration 64-1 shows a reinforced masonry wall using hollow units (concrete blocks).

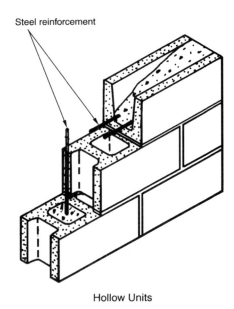

Steel reinforcement

Hollow Units

Illustration 64-1. Reinforced masonry wall using hollow masonry units.

1. Assemble the tools and materials needed to build this demonstration wall. Arrange your work area and snap a chalk line on the floor to maintain the location of the wall. Lay down a full mortar bed for the concrete blocks. Lay the first course of blocks as shown in Illustration 64-1.   Completed ☐

2. Lay the second course of blocks as shown in the illustration. Fill the exposed cell in the blocks on the first course and insert a 1/2 diameter rebar.   Completed ☐

3. Lay the top course using a lintel block. Place two 3/8" diameter pieces of rebar in the lintel block. Add some mortar to hold the bars in place. Use a board across the end to hold back the mortar. Support it with a couple of concrete blocks.   Completed ☐

4. Strike the joints and brush the blocks. Inspect your work.   Completed ☐

Name_____

Reinforced masonry wall using solid units (brick)

Illustration 64-2 shows a reinforced masonry wall using solid units (brick).

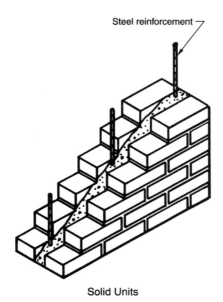

Illustration 64-2. Reinforced masonry wall using solid units.

1. Assemble the tools and materials needed to build this demonstration wall. Arrange your work area and snap a chalk line on the floor to maintain the location of the wall. Lay down a full mortar bed for the back wythe of bricks. Lay the back wythe as shown in Illustration 64-2.   Completed ❑

2. Lay the front wythe of brick exactly as the back wythe. Tool the joints and brush the wall.   Completed ❑

3. Fill the void with mortar as shown in the illustration. Place a board across the end to hold the mortar. Support the board with a concrete block.   Completed ❑

4. Insert three 1/2″ diameter rebars vertically in the space between the wythes.   Completed ❑

5. Examine your work, clean up the area, and return the tools and materials to their assigned places.   Completed ❑

Instructor's Initials:_____

Date: _____

Job Practice 64 Review ■━━━━━━━━━━━━━━━

After completing this job successfully, answer the following questions correctly:

1. How is grout used in a reinforced masonry wall when bricks are the masonry units? _____

   _____

   _____

2. How is grout used in a reinforced masonry wall when hollow concrete blocks are the masonry units?

   _____

3. What is the minimum amount of steel reinforcing that must be used in a reinforced masonry wall?

   _____

   _____

4. What size vertical and horizontal rebar was used in the concrete block wall? _____

   _____

5. No horizontal reinforcing was used in the wall that was made from brick. Is horizontal reinforcing sometimes used in this wall type? Why? _____

   _____

   _____

Score: _____

Job Practice **65**

Installing Steel and Concrete Reinforced Lintels

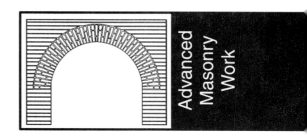

Advanced Masonry Work

Name_____

Date_____

Instructor _____

Period _____

Objective

After you have completed this job you will be able to install steel lintels in brick veneer and concrete reinforced lintels in concrete block walls using proper technique.

Equipment

To complete this job you will need the following tools and materials:

- ❖ Mason's tools
- ❖ Mortar
- ❖ Supply of bricks
- ❖ Supply of blocks
- ❖ One steel angle 3″ × 3″ × 1/4″ by 56″ long
- ❖ One concrete reinforced lintel 7 5/8″ × 7 5/8″ × 64″
- ❖ Two thin sheet metal shims 6″ × 8″
- ❖ Hard hat, safety glasses, etc.

Recommended Procedure

Study the appropriate section in Chapter 13 (Construction Details) before starting this job.

Masonry above an opening must be supported with a lintel. Steel angles are generally used in brick and stone veneer walls. Precast concrete lintels or lintels made from lintel blocks are frequently used in concrete block walls. Whatever the type or application, the lintel should be stiff enough to resist bending in excess of 1/360th of the span.

This job will provide an opportunity to learn how to install a steel angle in a brick veneer wall and a precast concrete lintel in a concrete block wall.

Steel angle in a brick veneer wall

1. Assemble the tools and materials needed to build two sections of a single wythe of bricks each three bricks in length with a space between them of 48″. The total assembly will be five courses high.   Completed ☐

2. Snap a chalk line to locate the face of the wythe. Locate the center of the chalk line and measure off 24″ in each direction along the line. This 48″ distance will be the length of the opening in the wall.   Completed ☐

3. Lay three bricks on either side of the "opening". Lay a second course in running bond on the first course. Lay a third course to bring the wall segments up to 8″ in height.   Completed ☐

4. Strike the joints. Carefully set the steel angle across the openings such that it is supported 4″ on either end.   Completed ☐

5. Trim the sharp edge off several bricks along the edge that will sit in the radius on the steel angle. Lay the fourth course of bricks along the entire wall.   Completed ☐

6. Lay the fifth course of bricks to complete the wall. Strike the mortar joints and brush the wall.   Completed ☐

Precast concrete lintel in a concrete block wall

1. Assemble the tools and materials needed to build two sections of an 8″ concrete block wall each 24″ long with a 48″ space between. The total assembly will be 3 courses high.   Completed ☐

2. Snap a chalk line to locate the face of the wall. Locate the center of the chalk line and measure off 24″ in each direction along the line. This 48″ distance will be the length of the opening in the wall.   Completed ☐

3. Lay one block and a half block on either side of the "opening". Lay a second course in running bond. Strike the joints. Let the mortar cure for several hours before proceeding to the next step.   Completed ☐

4. Place a sheet metal shim on the top of the blocks nearest the opening. This will provide support for the concrete lintel. Place the mortar, then get someone to help you set the lintel into place. It should be 8″ longer on either end than the opening.   Completed ☐

5. Check the lintel to be sure it is level and positioned properly. Complete the course. Strike the joints and brush the wall.   Completed ☐

6. Inspect your work, clean up the area, and return all tools and materials to their assigned places.   Completed ☐

Instructor's Initials:_____

Date: _____

Name_____

Job Practice 65 Review ▰▰▰▰▰▰▰▰▰▰▰▰▰▰▰▰

After completing this job successfully, answer the following questions correctly:

1. What is the function of a lintel? _____

   _____

2. What kind of lintels are frequently used in concrete block walls? _____

   _____

3. What type of lintel is generally used in brick and stone veneer walls? _____

   _____

4. What is the maximum bending allowed in lintels regardless of their type? _____

   _____

5. What is the recommended length of support at either end of a steel angle lintel? _____

   _____

6. What is the function of the sheet metal skin at either end of the concrete lintel? _____

   _____

Score: _____

Job Practice 66

Building Reinforced Concrete Block and Brick Lintels

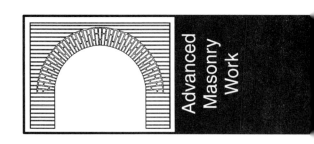

Advanced Masonry Work

Name_____

Date_____

Instructor_____

Period_____

Objective

After you have completed this job you will be able to build reinforced concrete block and brick lintels using proper technique.

Equipment

To complete this job you will need the following tools and materials:

- ❖ Mason's tools
- ❖ Mortar
- ❖ Supply of lintel blocks
- ❖ Supply of bricks
- ❖ Supply of reinforcing steel bars
- ❖ Four pieces of plywood, 12″ × 16″
- ❖ Hard hat, safety glasses, etc.

Recommended Procedure

Study the appropriate section in Chapter 13 (Construction Details) before starting this job.

Reinforced masonry lintels (brick and block) are becoming more popular because the steel is completely protected from the elements and the initial cost is less because less steel is required.

This job will provide an opportunity to build a reinforced brick lintel and a reinforced concrete block lintel to learn the basic procedure. The design of reinforced lintels, however, should be left to engineers and architects. The products of this job could be used for load testing and experimentation after they have cured for 28 days.

Reinforced Concrete Block Lintel

1. Assemble the tools and materials required to build a reinforced concrete block lintel that is 8″ × 8″ × 48″.

Completed ❑

2. Lay three concrete lintel blocks end to end on the floor with mortar between each. Tool the joints. Illustration 66-1 shows a section of the lintel.

Completed ☐

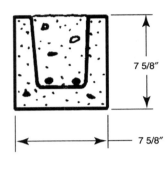

7 5/8″

7 5/8″

Lintel Block

Illustration 66-1. Section of a reinforced concrete block lintel.

3. Place a piece of plywood at each end of the assembly with a block against the boards to prevent the mortar from leaking out.

Completed ☐

4. Place about 1/2″ thick mortar bed in the lintel blocks to be sure the rebars are completely embedded. Lay in two pieces of rebar 3/8″ diameter by 48″ long. See the drawing.

Completed ☐

5. Completely fill the lintel block cavity with mortar or grout. Work it into all crevices. Smooth the top.

Completed ☐

6. Allow the assembly to cure for several days before moving it. Use the lintel for load testing.

Completed ☐

Reinforced brick masonry lintel

1. Assemble the tools and materials required to build a reinforced brick lintel that is 8″ wide by 5 courses high by 48″ long.

Completed ☐

2. Lay the bed courses of brick on the floor with full head and collar joints. Do not use a bed joint as the assembly will be moved later. Refer to Illustration 66-2.

Completed ☐

Name_____

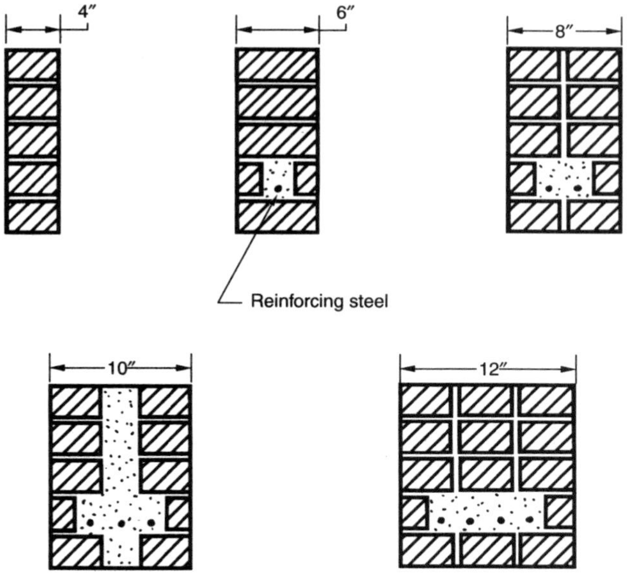

Illustration 66-2. Reinforced brick masonry lintels.

3. Cut several bricks lengthwise for the second course of brick. Lay the second course of queen closures. Place a piece of plywood at each end to contain the grouted cavity.   Completed ❑

4. Lay a mortar bed between the wythes about 1″ thick. Work it into the cracks and crevices. Place two 3/8″ rebars as shown in the illustration for 8″ lintel. The rebar should extend the full length of the lintel.   Completed ❑

5. Fill the cavity with mortar and work it into all spaces and voids. Smooth off the top.   Completed ❑

6. Lay the next three courses with full bed, head, and collar joints. The total assembly must act as a single unit to be effective. Tool the joints and brush the bricks.   Completed ❑

7. Do not move the lintel for several days. Then it may be used for load tests.   Completed ❑

8. Inspect your work, clean up the area, and return all tools and materials to their assigned places.   Completed ❑

Instructor's Initials:_____

Date: _____

Job Practice 66 Review ▬▬▬▬▬▬▬▬▬▬▬▬▬▬▬▬▬

After completing this job successfully, answer the following questions correctly:

1. Why are brick lintels less expensive? _____

_____

2. What are two reasons not to select a brick lintel? _____

_____

_____

3. Why are special lintel blocks needed to build a concrete block lintel? _____

_____

_____

4. How many days are required for concrete or mortar to cure? _____

_____

5. What was the most time consuming operation in building a brick lintel? _____

_____

6. What is the most likely reason for failure of a brick lintel? _____

_____

Score: _____

Job Practice 67
Building Masonry Sills
and Installing Stone Sills

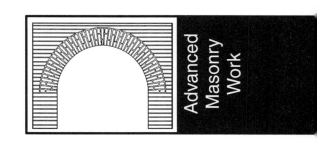

Name_____

Date_____

Instructor _____

Period _____

Objective

After you have completed this job you will be able to build masonry sills and install stone sills using proper technique.

Equipment

To complete this job you will need the following tools and materials:

- ❖ Mason's tools
- ❖ Mortar
- ❖ Supply of bricks
- ❖ One stone sill
- ❖ Section of frame wall with opening
- ❖ Hard hat, safety glasses, etc.

Recommended Procedure

Study the appropriate section in Chapter 13 (Construction Details) before starting this job.

The primary function of a sill is to channel water away from the building. The sill may consist of a single unit or multiple units. It may be built in place or prefabricated. It may be made from a variety of materials—brick, stone, concrete, metal. Single units are either slip sills or lug sills. See Illustration 67-1.

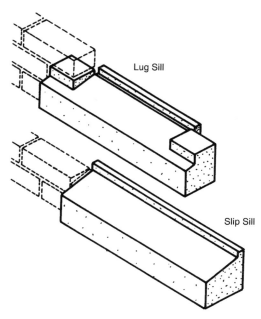

Illustration 67-1. A one-piece lug and slip sill.

A slip sill may be left out when the opening is being laid and set at a later time, but the lug sill should be set when the masonry is up to the bottom of the opening. Brick sills may be installed during or after the face bricks are laid.

This job will provide an opportunity to lay a brick sill using rowlock headers and install a stone slip sill in a brick veneered wall.

Brick masonry sill

1. Assemble the tools and materials needed to lay a short veneered wall and install a brick masonry sill. Study Illustration 67-2 to see how a brick sill is constructed.

Completed

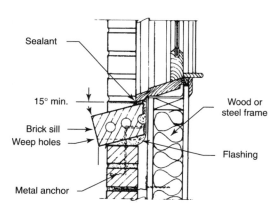

Illustration 67-2. Brick sill in a veneered wall on frame backup. (BIA)

Name_____

2. Using a frame wall backup, lay the veneer up to three courses above the bottom of the window opening.   Completed ❏

3. Set bricks on edge in the opening where the sill will be built to determine proper spacing. Make note of the mortar joint thickness required. Thinner mortar joints are preferred over large ones.   Completed ❏

4. Cut enough bricks to build the sill. Refer to the drawing again.   Completed ❏

5. Install flashing to shed water and prevent mortar from falling into the air space. Apply a generous mortar bed and lay the rowlock headers. Be sure the head joints are full.   Completed ❏

6. Tool the joints and brush the bricks. Inspect your work to be sure it meets the desired standards.   Completed ❏

Stone slip sill

1. Assemble the tools and materials needed to install a slip sill in a brick veneered wall on frame backup. Study Illustration 67-3 to see how a stone slip sill is positioned in the wall.   Completed ❏

Illustration 67-3. Stone slip sill in a brick veneered wall on frame backup.

2. Using a frame wall backup, lay the veneer up to three courses below the window opening. Measure the sill to determine the desired height of masonry to mount the sill at the proper height. Masonry units may have to be cut so the spacing works out right. Prior planning can eliminate this problem.   Completed ❏

3. Complete the veneer to the desired height to set the sill. Set the sill in a full mortar bed. Be sure it is level and positioned properly with respect to the bottom of the window.   Completed ❏

4. Continue three more courses of veneer on either side of the window. Strike the joints and brush the wall.   Completed ❏

5. Examine your work, clean up the area, and return all tools
and materials to their assigned places.   Completed ☐

Instructor's Initials:_____

Date: _____

Job Practice 67 Review ▬▬▬▬▬▬▬▬▬▬▬▬▬▬▬▬

After completing this job successfully, answer the following questions correctly:

1. What is the function of a sill? _____
   _____
   _____

2. What three materials are used most frequently for sills in masonry construction? _____
   _____

3. What are the basic differences between a slip sill and a lug sill? _____
   _____
   _____
   _____
   _____
   _____

4. A brick sill is neither a slip or lug sill, but composed of several units. When is the appropriate time
   to build a brick sill?_____
   _____
   _____

5. What position are bricks usually laid in when forming a sill?_____
   _____

6. When planning for a stone sill, what is the critical height dimension location? _____
   _____
   _____

Score: _____

Job Practice 68
Building a Brick Masonry Arch

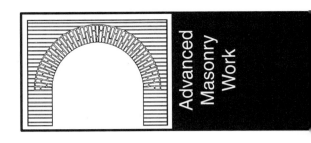

Name_____

Date_____

Instructor_____

Period_____

Objective

After you have completed this job you will be able to build a brick masonry arch using proper technique.

Equipment

To complete this job you will need the following tools and materials:

- ❖ Mason's tools
- ❖ Mortar
- ❖ Supply of bricks
- ❖ Supply of 8 penny nails
- ❖ Construction lumber to build support centering
- ❖ Hard hat, safety glasses, etc.

Recommended Procedure

Study the appropriate section in Chapter 13 (Construction Details) before starting this job.

Arches have been used for centuries to span openings. Some have been built which span distances over 130′. Several types are used in modern construction. The terminology related to arches is unique and should be mastered to be truly proficient in arch construction.

An arch is normally classified by the curve of its intrados (the curve which bounds the lower edge of the arch) and by its function, shape, or architectural style. Arches are classified as major and minor arches. Minor arches have spans that do not exceed 6′ with a maximum rise-to-span ratio of 0.15. The jack and segmental arches seem to be the most popular types used today.

This job will provide an opportunity to build a segmental arch in an 8″ solid brick wall. The arch will use the centering built for Job Practice 56. The arch will be 36″ wide with a rise of 3″. See Illustration 68-1.

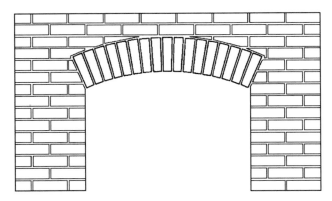

Illustration 68-1. Typical segmental arch.

1. Assemble the tools and materials needed for this job. Arrange a work area and examine the centering already constructed or construct your own following the procedure described in Job Practice 56.   Completed ☐

2. Snap a chalk line to establish a wall 6' long and 8" thick. The 36" wide arch will be centered in the wall. Mark the location of the arch in the wall.   Completed ☐

3. Lay five courses of bricks on each side of the arch. Be sure these bricks have full bed and head joints, because they will support the weight of the masonry above the arch.   Completed ☐

4. Measure the distance from the floor to the top of the fifth (top) course of bricks. Subtract from that dimension the height of the centering at the end. Cut four pieces of 2" × 4" lumber to support the ends of the centering (two under each end).   Completed ☐

5. Tack the support pieces to the rib boards. You will need to pull these nails when you remove the centering. Check the assembly to be sure it is plumb and steady. You may have to shim one or more legs to produce a solid platform for work.   Completed ☐

6. Lay the centering on its side and place bricks in a soldier course around the arch curve to determine the proper spacing. The bricks should have very narrow mortar joints at the bottom, but not touch. Mark the position of each brick on the form.   Completed ☐

7. Insert the assembled centering and support legs between the two wall sections. Be careful not to disturb them. If you do, take them down and begin again.   Completed ☐

8. Lay the back wythe first. Place one or two bricks on the left and then on the right side. Work from both sides toward the middle.   Completed ☐

9. Follow the same procedure in laying the bricks on the front wythe. Be sure to fill the collar joint. Try not to let mortar squeeze out too much on the bottom side of the units. These joints must be pointed later.   Completed ☐

10. Tool the joints and check the appearance of the arch. If it is not uniform and clean, tear it down and begin again.   Completed ☐

Name_____

1. Complete the wall until it reaches a height that is two courses above the highest point of the arch. Notice that you will have to cut several bricks to fit the curve. Measure twice and cut once. This is the most difficult part of the job.   Completed ❏

2. Tool the joints and brush the wall.   Completed ❏

3. When the mortar has cured a few days, remove the shims and nails from the supports from beneath the centering and carefully remove them. Get someone to help you. Do not let the centering fall.   Completed ❏

4. Remove excess mortar from the bottom of the arch and point any joints that need it.   Completed ❏

Instructor's Initials:_____

Date: _____

Job Practice 68 Review ▬▬▬▬▬▬▬▬▬▬▬▬▬▬▬▬▬▬

After completing this job successfully, answer the following questions correctly:

1. Identify four bases for the classification of arches._____

_____

_____

2. Most arches used in residential or commercial construction today are minor arches. What is a minor arch?_____

_____

_____

3. If someone has not already prepared a pattern of the arch curve for you, how could you scribe the curve on a piece of cardboard using tools and materials that a mason has in their tool bag? _____

_____

_____

4. Why is the centering for the arch built 1″ less than the thickness of the wall? _____

_____

_____

5. What is the purpose of the keystone? _____

_____

_____

Score:_____

Job Practice 69

Forming Movement Joints in Concrete and Masonry

Advanced Masonry Work

Name_____

Date_____

Instructor _____

Period _____

Objective

After you have completed this job you will be able to form movement joints in concrete and masonry using proper technique.

Equipment

To complete this job you will need the following tools and materials:

- ❖ Mason's tools
- ❖ Mortar
- ❖ Supply of bricks
- ❖ Supply of concrete blocks
- ❖ Elastic expansion joint materials
- ❖ Concrete
- ❖ Form material (2″ × 4″)
- ❖ Shovel
- ❖ Control joint blocks
- ❖ Hard hat, safety glasses, etc.

Recommended Procedure

Study the appropriate section in Chapter 13 (Construction Details) before starting this job.

Because all materials in a building experience changes in volume, a system of movement joints is necessary to allow these movements to occur. Failure to permit these movements may result in cracks in masonry construction. There are various types of movement joints in buildings: expansion joints, control joints, building expansion joints, and construction joints. Each type of movement joint is designed to perform a specific task, and they should not be used interchangeably.

Expansion joint

An expansion joint is used to separate brick masonry into segments to prevent cracking due to changes in temperature, moisture expansion, elastic deformation due to loads, and creep. Expansion joints may be horizontal or vertical. The joints are formed of highly elastic materials placed in a continuous, unobstructed opening, through each wythe. See Illustration 69-1.

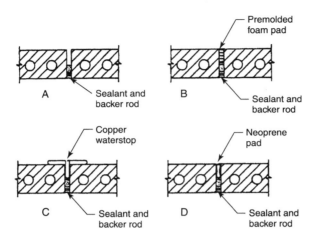

Illustration 69-1. Typical expansion joints in brick masonry.

1. Lay a short single wythe wall six units long in running bond, but include a vertical expansion joint in the center of the wall. The joint should be the same width as a regular mortar joint. Some bricks will have to be cut.   Completed ☐

2. Apply an elastic expansion joint material to the joint. Follow the manufacturer's instructions.   Completed ☐

Control joint in concrete

A control joint is used in concrete or concrete masonry to create a plane of weakness which, used in conjunction with reinforcement or joint reinforcement, controls the location of cracks due to volume changes resulting from shrinkage and creep. A control joint may be made of inelastic materials. A control joint will open rather than close.

1. Build a form from 2" x 4" lumber to cast a flat slab 8' ft. long by 1' wide by 3 1/2" thick on a level surface. Form an anchor in the soil at each end by digging a hole in the ground 12" to 14" deep.   Completed ☐

2. Fill the form with concrete and finish the slab in the normal manner. Cut a control joint at the midpoint.   Completed ☐

3. Observe the control joint periodically to note any separation at the control joint.   Completed ☐

Name_____

Control joint in concrete masonry

A special concrete masonry unit is available that controls volume change in a wall. Placed at specific intervals, this block relieves stress in the wall. See Illustration 69-2.

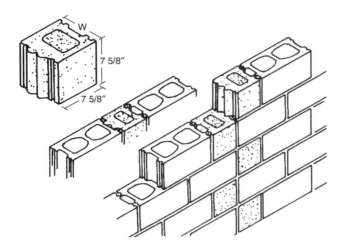

Illustration 69-2. Special concrete block designed to relieve stresses in a wall.

1. Lay a concrete block wall 48″ long with a vertical control joint at the center point of the wall. Use regular 8″ × 8″ × 16″ stretchers and 8″ × 8″ × 8″ control joint blocks as shown in the illustration. Lay the wall three courses high.

   Completed ❏

2. Rake out the mortar along the control joint and fill with elastic expansion joint material. Tool the other joints and brush the wall.

   Completed ❏

   Illustration 69-3 shows a control joint in masonry construction.

Illustration 69-3. A typical building control joint.

Instructor's Initials:_____

Date: _____

Job Practice 69 Review ▬▬▬▬▬▬▬▬▬▬

After completing this job successfully, answer the following questions correctly:

1. Why are movement joints necessary in concrete and masonry structures? _____

_____

_____

2. Name several types of movement joints that may be used in a building. _____

_____

_____

3. What kind of material is placed in an expansion joint? _____

_____

4. How does a control joint in a concrete slab work?_____

_____

_____

_____

5. Who should plan the location of building expansion joints?_____

_____

Score: _____

Job Practice **70**
Installing Masonry Pavers on a Rigid Base

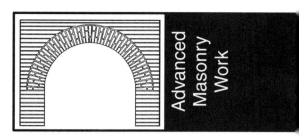

Name_____

Date_____

Instructor _____

Period _____

Objective

After you have completed this job you will be able to install masonry pavers on a rigid base using proper technique.

Equipment

To complete this job you will need the following tools and materials:

- ❖ Mason's tools
- ❖ Mortar
- ❖ Supply of pavers
- ❖ Existing concrete slab
- ❖ Masonry saw
- ❖ Hard hat, safety glasses, etc.

Recommended Procedure

Study the appropriate section in Chapter 13 (Construction Details) before starting this job.

Masonry paving systems can be installed with mortar (rigid) or without mortar (flexible or *hand-tight*). Most standard pavers used with mortar allow for a 3/8" mortar joint. Rigid systems must be installed on a rigid base. A concrete slab usually provides this base. See Illustration 70-1

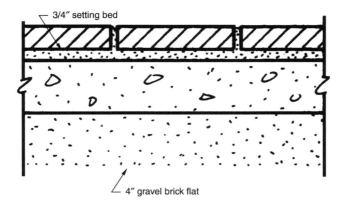

Illustration 70-1. Section through pavers on concrete slab.

This job will provide an opportunity to pave a 6' square area on a concrete slab.

1. If an existing concrete stab is not available, then form and pour a 6' square slab for this job. Assemble the necessary tools and materials to install pavers on the slab.   Completed ❑

2. Select any concrete, brick, or clay paver that you like. Choose an appropriate pattern bond and place the pavers on the slab without mortar to determine the best arrangement. Some pavers may need to be cut to center the pattern on the slab.   Completed ❑

3. When the arrangement and spacing have been decided upon, mix the mortar. Masonry cement is often not recommended by manufacturers of pavers.   Completed ❑

4. Provide a solid bed joint of mortar about 3/4" thick and lay the pavers along one side. Be sure the spacing is uniform. If pavers need to be cut, use the masonry saw.   Completed ❑

5. Lay the pavers along adjacent sides. Then fill in the remaining space working from these two sides.   Completed ❑

6. When moving around on the pavers while the mortar is wet, use large pieces of 3/4" plywood to spread the load. Tool the joints and clean off any mortar on the pavers with a damp sponge. Do not sponge the mortar joints.   Completed ❑

7. Inspect your work, clean up the area, and return all tools and materials to their assigned places.   Completed ❑

Instructor's Initials:_____

Date: _____

Name_____

Job Practice 70 Review ▬▬▬▬▬▬▬▬▬▬▬▬▬

After completing this job successfully, answer the following questions correctly:

1. Masonry pavers may be placed on a rigid or flexible base. What primary factor should be considered in deciding which to use? _____
   _____

2. Why must a rigid base be used if the pavers are to have mortar between the joints? _____
   _____
   _____
   _____

3. How can fresh mortar be removed from pavers?_____
   _____
   _____

4. When laying pavers on a rigid base, how thick a bed joint is recommended?_____
   _____

5. The base is important for a flexible installation. Describe the recommended type base for hand-tight units. _____
   _____
   _____
   _____
   _____

Score:_____

Job Practice **71**
Building Concrete and Masonry Steps

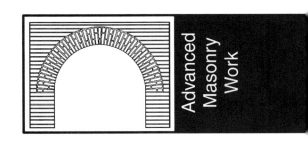

Advanced Masonry Work

Name_____

Date_____

Instructor _____

Period _____

Objective

After you have completed this job you will be able to build concrete and masonry steps using proper technique.

Equipment

To complete this job you will need the following tools and materials:

- ❖ Mason's tools
- ❖ Materials for concrete
- ❖ Concrete mixer
- ❖ Form materials
- ❖ Bricks or pavers
- ❖ Shovel
- ❖ Concrete finishing tools
- ❖ A sloping site
- ❖ Hard hat, safety glasses, etc.
- ❖ Sketch pad

Recommended Procedure

Study the appropriate section in Chapter 13 (Construction Details) before starting this job.

This job will provide an opportunity to build a simple set of steps similar to those shown in Illustration 71-1. This is a good class project.

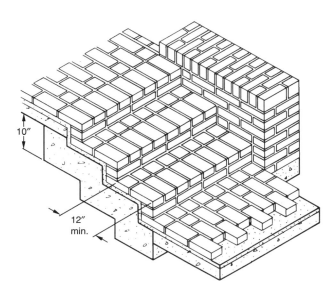

Illustration 71-1. Typical brick steps laid over a concrete foundation.

1. Assemble the tools and materials needed to prepare the foundation excavation and forms for the concrete base for a set of steps similar to the illustration above.   Completed ☐

2. Using a sketch pad, record the drop in elevation where you plan to build the steps. Plan the steps around this information. Be sure to follow good design principles. For example, the ideal riser height is about 7″ while the ideal tread width is about 12″. Plan the stairs in such a way that masonry unit sizes are also taken into consideration. Ask your instructor to check out your plan.   Completed ☐

3. When the plan is complete and acceptable, begin excavation for the foundation and build the forms. Check the dimensions several times to be sure you have followed your plan.   Completed ☐

4. Mix the concrete and place it in the forms. Rod or vibrate the concrete to be sure all voids are filled. Leave the surface slightly rough so the mortar will stick to it.   Completed ☐

5. When the concrete has cured for several days, remove the forms and examine your work. Lay out one step without mortar to check the spacing. Then, mix some mortar and lay the units on the lowest level first. Work your way up the steps.   Completed ☐

6. Be sure not to bump any of the previously laid units. Tool the joints as the mortar hardens to the proper degree. Brush the bricks. Use a damp sponge to remove any mortar smears on the bricks. Do not sponge the mortar joints.   Completed ☐

7. Build the walls on either side of the steps using any pattern that you desire.   Completed ☐

Name_____

8. Tool all mortar joints and brush the bricks. Check over the whole job and admire your project. Congratulations, you designed the project and built it "from the ground up."   Completed ☐

9. Smooth the grade around the steps and return all tools and materials to their assigned places.   Completed ☐

Instructor's Initials:_____

Date: _____

Job Practice 71 Review ▬▬▬▬▬▬▬▬▬▬▬▬▬▬▬

After completing this job successfully, answer the following questions correctly:

1. When planning a set of steps as in this job, why is it necessary to know the total rise of the steps?

_____

_____

_____

_____

2. What is the ideal riser height of a step?_____

_____

3. As the riser height increases from 7″ to 9″ what should happen to the tread width? _____

_____

4. Why is building a good solid foundation necessary for a set of steps? _____

_____

_____

_____

_____

5. What type of bricks should be used for steps or paving in climates that experience freezing?_____

_____

Score: _____

Job Practice 72
Building a Masonry Fireplace and Chimney

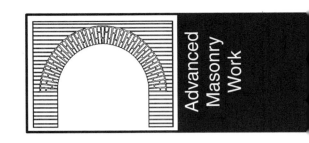

Name_____

Date_____

Instructor_____

Period_____

Objective

After you have completed this job you will be able to build a masonry fireplace and chimney using proper technique.

Equipment

To complete this job you will need the following tools and materials:

- ❖ Mason's tools
- ❖ Mortar
- ❖ Supply of bricks
- ❖ Fire bricks
- ❖ Damper
- ❖ Lintel (angle steel)
- ❖ Supply of concrete blocks
- ❖ Fire clay
- ❖ Flue liners
- ❖ Flue blocks
- ❖ Pad of graph paper
- ❖ Hard hat, safety glasses, etc.

Recommended Procedure ▬▬▬▬▬▬▬▬▬▬▬▬▬▬▬▬▬▬▬▬▬▬ ▬

Study the appropriate section in Chapter 13 (Construction Details) before starting this job.

The masonry fireplace has been around for a long time, and even though many have turned to stoves, gas logs, or imitation fireplaces, a truly functional masonry fireplace is hard to beat.

This job should be a class project in a realistic setting—a home under construction. If this isn't possible, the project can be performed in the lab. Rather than plan every detail for you, you will have to do the planning. The basic operation will be presented to keep you on track. Be sure to study the section on Fireplace and Chimney Construction in your text before starting this job. Become familiar with the parts of a fireplace and the terminology. Good luck!

1. The most popular and functional fireplace for most residential settings is a single face fireplace with an opening about 36″ wide and 29″ high. Turn to the chart in your text, "Specifications for fireplace opening height, hearth size, and flue size." You will see that a 36″ wide × 29″ high opening requires a 16″ hearth and 12″ × 12″ flue liners. The damper for this fireplace is 40″ on the outside of the front flange, but tapers back to 32 3/4″ on the back. Continue studying the fireplace specifications until you feel sure you have the dimensions you will need to build it.   Completed ❑

2. Study the section drawing in Illustration 72-1. It shows the structure from the footing to the chimney cap. The drawing shows every brick. Try to visualize building it. When you can do this you are ready to begin the construction.   Completed ❑

Name_____

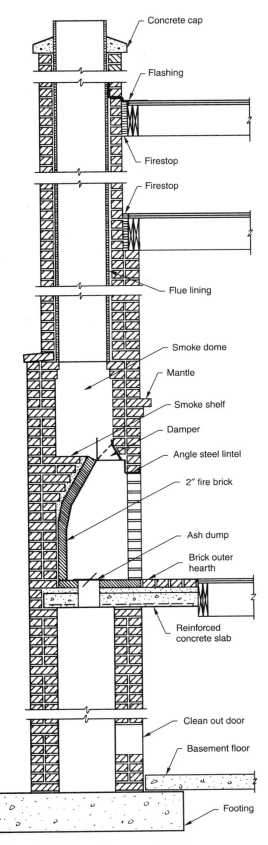

Illustration 72-1. Fireplace and Chimney Components.

3. Sketch a plan view of the fireplace on graph paper to scale. Make the drawing large enough so that details can be represented. A scale of 1/8" = 1" would fit on 8 1/2" × 11" paper if it were turned sideways. Include brick sizes in your plan. You may have to do some research. For example, what are the dimensions of a firebrick? What size mortar joint is used with firebrick? What is fire clay? What are the code requirements in your area related to masonry fireplaces? These are good class discussion topics. Complete your plan.

Completed ❏

4. Notice that the foundation for a chimney is larger and thicker than a typical foundation wall footing. This is because the fireplace and chimney are very heavy and, therefore, need a large footing. One other point, the fireplace/chimney should be a freestanding structure. Framing should not be closer than 2" to the chimney. Build the foundation for your fireplace using concrete blocks, bricks, or a combination.

Completed ❏

5. Be careful as you approach the floor level. You should plan the elevation (height) of the outer and inner hearth. Will it be raised or level with the finished floor as the illustration shows? Plan it the way you want it to be and then work your plan. In olden times, the outer hearth was supported by corbelling out the bricks, but few people do that any more. You could do that, but probably should plan for a reinforced slab. Complete the job to the floor level.

Completed ❏

6. Don't install the bricks on the outer hearth until last, because it will be covered in mortar by the time the job is finished. Place the firebricks on the inner hearth. These units should be arranged with the ash dump as the central feature. Locate its placement and then arrange the firebricks. Lay them on a thick mortar bed with fire clay between them. Read the instructions on the can or bucket. Let the bricks on the hearth run beyond the inside dimensions of the firebox to support the firebricks that line the firebox.

Completed ❏

7. Bring up the sides of the firebox and chimney to the level where the back begins to slope forward. This is where the job gets tricky. You will have to cut the fire brick to fit the angles formed by the tapered sides and sloping back. Be sure to fill in the space behind and beside the liner with mortar and pieces of bricks or blocks. Prop up the sloping firebricks as you bring them up to the level of the damper.

Completed ❏

8. Once you reach the height of the front opening (29") you will need to install the 3" × 4" × 1/4" angle steel. Trim off the back edge of the brick so they will fit properly against the angle steel lintel. Set the angle directly on the course of bricks beneath it so it can move as it heats up and cools down. Lay a couple of courses above the opening and then install the damper. If you calculated accurately, the damper will cover the opening. If not, you will have to tear it out and start again.

Completed ❏

Name_____

9. Continue building the chimney until you reach the mantle level. You don't have to have a mantle, but at least consider it while you can. Corbel the bricks at the top of the smoke chamber until the opening is the size of the inside dimensions of the flue liner. Wait until the mortar has hardened some before setting the first flue liner on its supports.   Completed ❑

10. Set the first flue liner and support it on all sides as you lay up the chimney. Frequently, the width of the chimney is racked back once the masonry clears the height of the fireplace. This is an option, but not a necessity.   Completed ❑

11. Continue laying up the chimney and flue liners until the desired height is reached. Build a form around the top of the chimney and pour the chimney cap. The top flue liner should protrude a couple of inches above the top of the cap.   Completed ❑

12. Complete the outer hearth. Tool the joints and brush the bricks. Be proud of your work and strive to do it better each time.   Completed ❑

Instructor's Initials:_____

Date: _____

Job Practice 72 Review ▰▰▰▰▰▰▰▰▰▰▰▰▰▰▰▰

After completing this job successfully, answer the following questions correctly:

1. If the opening size of a fireplace is increased, what effect does that have on the flue size and/or height of the chimney? _____

_____

_____

_____

_____

_____

2. What part of a traditional masonry fireplace is most responsible for reflecting heat into the room?

_____

_____

3. Why is the fireplace/chimney a freestanding structure?_____

_____

_____

_____

4. In some older fireplaces regular bricks were used to line the firebox. Why is that not a recommended practice today? _____

_____

_____

_____

5. What material is modern masonry flue liners made from? _____

_____

6. How should a masonry flue liner be cut if it becomes necessary? _____

_____

_____

Score: _____

Job Practice 73
Building a Masonry Garden Wall with Coping

Advanced Masonry Work

Name_____

Date_____

Instructor _____

Period _____

Objective

After you have completed this job you will be able to build a masonry garden wall with a coping using proper technique.

Equipment

To complete this job you will need the following tools and materials:

- ❖ Mason's tools
- ❖ Mortar
- ❖ Supply of bricks or blocks
- ❖ Stone or molded brick coping
- ❖ Concrete footing
- ❖ Hard hat, safety glasses, etc.

Recommended Procedure

Study the appropriate section in Chapter 13 (Construction Details) before you begin this job.

There are many types of garden walls (freestanding structures)—perforated walls, straight walls, pier and panel walls, and serpentine walls. Each has its particular application and style.

This job will provide an opportunity to build a panel type garden wall of your own design. The only specifications are that the wall should be 6′ in length, 4′ high, rest on a footing, terminate with a 12″ square post at each end, and be made from brick or block masonry.

1. Using graph paper, make a drawing of the garden wall panel that you plan to build. Your drawing should be accurate and complete, because the finished product will be compared to your drawing. Design your wall.

   Completed ❑

2. Show your design to your instructor and get his/her approval before beginning the project.

   Completed ❑

3. Assemble the tools and materials needed for the project.

   Completed ❑

4. Build the wall using proper technique. Be sure to include reinforcing if it is necessary for your design. Refer to the text for recommendations to resist wind loads. See Illustration 73-1. below for ideas for finishing off the wall at the top.

Completed ❑

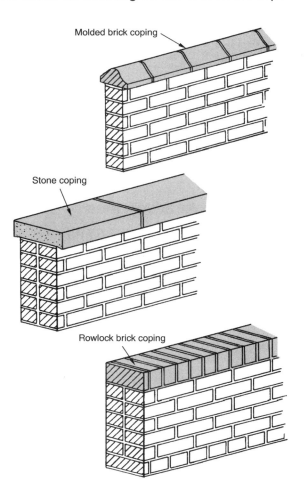

Illustration 73-1. Straight garden walls with three commonly used copings.

5. Discuss the strengths and weaknesses of your design with your instructor. Think about what you would do differently if you were building the wall a second time. Learn from your experience.

Completed ❑

Instructor's Initials:_____

Date: _____

Name_____

Job Practice 73 Review ▰▰▰▰▰▰▰▰▰▰▰▰▰▰▰▰▰▰

After completing this job successfully, answer the following questions correctly:

1. What are four popular types of garden walls? _____

_____

_____

2. Why is a footing or foundation that reaches below the frost line necessary for a quality garden wall?

_____

_____

_____

3. Steel reinforcing might not be necessary in short, thick walls. How can you determine whether or not reinforcing should be included in a wall that you plan to build?_____

_____

_____

4. What is the function of the coping on a garden wall? _____

_____

_____

_____

5. As a rule of thumb, what is the maximum height of an 8″ thick straight garden wall generally, without reinforcing?_____

_____

_____

_____

Score: _____

Job Practice **74**
Corbelling and Racking a Masonry Wall

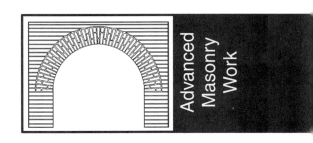

Advanced Masonry Work

Name_____

Date_____

Instructor_____

Period _____

Objective

After you have completed this job you will be able to build a masonry wall that includes corbelling and racking using proper technique.

Equipment

To complete this job you will need the following tools and materials:

- ❖ Mason's tools
- ❖ Mortar
- ❖ Supply of bricks
- ❖ Hard hat, safety glasses, etc.

Recommended Procedure

Study the appropriate section in Chapter 13 (Construction Details) before you begin this job.

A corbel is defined as a shelf or ledge formed by projecting successive courses of masonry out from the face of the wall. Racking is defined as masonry in which successive courses are stepped back from the face of the wall.

Generally, the total horizontal projection should not exceed one-half the thickness of a solid wall, or one-half the thickness of the veneer of a veneered wall. A single course should not exceed one-half of the unit height or one-third of the unit bed depth, whichever is less.

From these limitations, the minimum slope of the corbelling can be established as 63° and 26 minutes, measured from the horizontal to the face of the corbelled surface.

When racking, there is no limitation on the distance each unit may be racked so long as the cores of the units are not exposed.

This job will provide an opportunity to design a demonstration wall that includes a section of corbelled wall and a section of racked wall. The overall dimensions of the wall should be 12″ thick by 32″ long by twelve courses high. The structure should be stable.

1. Using a piece of graph paper, draw the plan view and elevations (side views) of "your" wall. Be sure you stay within the guidelines presented above. The rest is up to you.

Completed ☐

2. Discuss your plan with your instructor before building it. He/she may have some suggestions.   Completed ❑

3. Build your wall using your very best workmanship. Build something that you can be proud of. Take a photograph of the result and send it to the author of the text. Maybe he will include it in the next edition of the text. Best of luck!   Completed ❑

Instructor's Initials:_____

Date: _____

Job Practice 74 Review

After completing this job successfully, answer the following questions correctly:

1. Define *corbel*. _____

_____

_____

_____

_____

2. Describe *racking*. _____

_____

_____

3. The rules associated with corbelling are more stringent than for racking. Why is this?_____

_____

_____

_____

4. How far out can a corbel be extended in a solid wall?_____

_____

_____

5. How far may a unit be racked?_____

_____

_____

Score: _____

Job Practice 75
Building a Mortarless Retaining Wall

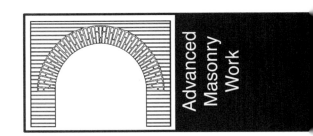

Name_____

Date_____

Instructor _____

Period _____

Objective

After you have completed this job you will be able to build a mortarless retaining wall with special masonry units designed for that purpose using proper technique.

Equipment

To complete this job you will need the following tools and materials:

- ❖ Level
- ❖ Shovel
- ❖ Crushed stone
- ❖ Sand
- ❖ Masonry units
- ❖ Dozen 1″ square stakes about 12″ long
- ❖ Mason's hammer
- ❖ Drain tile (optional)

Recommended Procedure

Study the appropriate section in Chapter 13 (Construction Details) before you begin this job.

A new concrete masonry unit that incorporates a lip on the backside has become very popular for retaining walls, tree rings, planters, and edgings. The lip provides proper alignment and prevents forward wall movement. Units are produced in straight or tapered designs. The tapered units are especially designed to form curved walls. See Illustration 75-1.

Illustration 75-1. Mortarless retaining wall using concrete masonry units.

Typical unit sizes include 6″ × 16″ × 12″, 6″ × 17 1/4″ × 12″, and 3″ × 17″ × 12″. Sizes vary from one manufacturer to another.

This job provides an opportunity to build a 6′ diameter tree ring, two courses high using this unique concrete masonry unit. This is a good community project for the class.

1. Select an appropriate subject (tree). Locate a 6′ diameter circle with the tree at the center. Mark the circle in some fashion.   Completed ❑

2. Remove some of the top soil to below the grass level. Using the level, locate the desired height of the first course. Drive a stake in the ground to that height. Transfer the height to the next stake and continue around the circle until you reach the starting point.   Completed ❑

3. Remove more soil to allow for a base of crushed stone for the masonry units. Add the crushed stone to the desired height. The surface of the stone should be level.   Completed ❑

4. Install the base course of tapered units. These units do not have a lip on the back. Level each unit and fill in around it with stone or sand. Remove the stakes as you proceed around the tree.   Completed ❑

5. Complete the base course. Add a drain tile behind the wall if necessary.   Completed ❑

6. Install the second course. These units should have a lip on the back edge to insure proper alignment. Stagger the joints. Complete this course.   Completed ❑

7. Backfill with top soil or sand. Do not pile soil up around the tree. Try to maintain the natural grade at the base of the tree.   Completed ❑

8. Admire your work. Clean up the area and return all tools and materials to their assigned places.   Completed ❑

Instructor's Initials:_____

Date: _____

Name_____

Job Practice 75 Review ▬▬▬▬▬▬▬▬▬▬▬▬▬▬▬

After completing this job successfully, answer the following questions correctly:

1. There seems to be one similar feature that is incorporated in all mortarless retaining walls. What is it?

_____

_____

_____

_____

2. Why is the foundation important in a mortarless retaining wall? _____

_____

_____

3. How could a construction level have been used to level the foundation for your tree ring project?

_____

_____

_____

_____

_____

4. What two functions did the lip on the lower back edge of the special concrete retaining wall units serve?_____

_____

_____

5. When would a drain tile be necessary in a retaining wall? _____

_____

_____

Score: _____

Job Practice 76
Using a Corner Pole

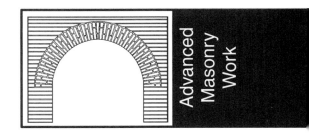

Advanced Masonry Work

Name_____

Date_____

Instructor _____

Period _____

Objective

After you have completed this job you will be able to use a typical corner pole for a particular job using proper technique.

Equipment

To complete this job you will need the following tools and materials:

- ❖ Mason's tools
- ❖ Mortar
- ❖ Supply of bricks
- ❖ Two corner poles and braces
- ❖ Pair of line blocks
- ❖ Mason's cord

Recommended Procedure

Study the appropriate section in Chapter 10 (Laying Brick) and Chapter 11 (Laying Block) before you begin this job.

The corner pole may be used instead of building leads when building a brick or block wall. Corner poles may be built by the mason or purchased. A sturdy aluminum corner pole with attached bracing is recommended.

This job will provide an opportunity for the apprentice mason to use a corner pole to lay a short (10 bricks long) single wythe brick wall in running bond to a height of 24″.

1. Collect the tools and materials needed for this job and arrange your work area. Completed ☐

2. Snap a chalk line about 10′ long where the wall is to be located. Completed ☐

3. Set up the corner poles at each end of the chalk line. Plumb and brace them in proper relation to the chalk line. Completed ☐

4. Lay out the first course in dry bond to mark the proper spacing. Completed ☐

5. Attach the line blocks and mason's cord to the corner poles at the proper height of the first course.   Completed ☐

6. Lay the first course of bricks to the line.   Completed ☐

7. Move the line up to the next course height and lay the second course of masonry.   Completed ☐

8. Continue the process until the wall is 24″ high.   Completed ☐

9. Tool the joints as the mortar hardens sufficiently. Brush the finished wall.   Completed ☐

10. Clean up the area and return the tools and materials to their proper places.   Completed ☐

Instructor's Initials:_____

Date: _____

Job Practice 76 Review

After completing this job successfully, answer the following questions correctly:

1. What advantages did you notice using the corner pole over building leads? _____
    _____
    _____
    _____

2. What disadvantages did you notice using the corner pole over building leads? _____
    _____
    _____

3. What situation does not lend itself to the use of corner poles? _____
    _____
    _____

4. What type of situation truly lends itself to the use of corner poles?_____
    _____
    _____

Score:_____